Louise L. Lambrichs was born to Belgian parents, both of whom were writers. She has had three novels published as well as two essays in the field of scientific research. She has been Literary Editor of *LaCroix* in Paris for the last fifteen years.

Siân Reynolds is a Professor of French at Stirling University. She is a writer and an editor and has translated several works from the French language.

HANNAH'S DIARY

LOUISE L. LAMBRICHS

Translated from the French by Siân Reynolds

Quartet Books

For Drazen

This book is supported by the French Ministry for Foreign Affairs, as part of the Burgess Programme headed for the French Embassy in London by the Institut Français du Royaume-Uni.

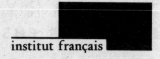

institut français

Published in Great Britain by Quartet Books Limited in 1998
A member of the Namara Group
27 Goodge Street
London W1P 2LD

A catalogue record for this book is available from the British Library

ISBN 0 7043 8081 1

Printed and bound in Great Britain by Cox & Wyman, Reading, Berks

1943

Wednesday 20 January

I think I must be pregnant again. Two months gone, maybe three. At first I took no notice. I thought my period was late because of everything that was happening – the unspeakable life we have been leading since the war began, the poor food, the shortages, the hardships. But now my breasts feel full and I feel sick from time to time. Robert has not noticed yet. It's true he has a lot to worry about and is not paying me much attention. The little time he spends at home he devotes to Colette. I can't complain. After all, these moments playing with her father may be the only good memories she will have of this miserable early childhood. When will this hell on earth end?

I have made an appointment with Dr Lebrun to check if I'm right. I haven't said anything to Robert yet.

Saturday 23 January

I've just come back from the doctor: yes, I am pregnant. When he told me, I began to cry. At first he thought I didn't want this child. But it was something else, a rush of emotion too strong for me. How can so much happiness still be possible? This child, all of a sudden, this life, hope, fighting back. A hope I am carrying. Can it be possible? I was crying but I wanted to laugh as well. I would have liked Robert to be there and take me in his arms, and be happy too, as in the old days.

Dr Lebrun was very kind. He agreed to treat me during the pregnancy and promised that when it was time he would refer me to a friend of his, an obstetrician at the Pitié Hospital. For now, he told me firmly that I should eat properly. Not so much for the baby, he pointed out, as for myself. The baby will take what it needs anyway. But if I don't eat properly, I might fall ill. I wonder how we are going to manage.

Coming out, I felt better. The tears comforted me, as if they were washing away the unhappiness that has built up over the years. I felt younger, more alive, almost euphoric. I'm sorry about one thing: Robert has left on business. He'll be away three days! Three days have never seemed so long. He'll probably telephone this evening, but I will say nothing about it. How could I? I want to see his expression when he hears, see a smile light up his face in a way I haven't seen for so many months now, and I want to see some hope in his eyes, hope that has been missing so long. Over the telephone, I would see none of that. And then there is the happiness of really feeling this news, of being filled with the reality of it, held in his arms, protected, the three of us in one person.

I went to fetch Colette from the child minder. I wanted to tell her the news, sweetheart you're going to have a little brother or sister, but I shouldn't yet, her father must be told first, we'll tell him together.

Sunday 24 January

I have dreamed about the baby for the first time. Just as it is at the moment, in my womb. The impression the dream left was both realistic and fantastic. I was going to the hospital to see the obstetrician and he asked me some questions, then asked me to lie down and felt my abdomen. Next he showed me a screen and said, 'Look, you're going to see your baby.' He put on a sort of grey overall with stripes and a hood with all kinds of electrical wires attached, and he put his ear to my abdomen; the screen lit up and I could see the baby. A foetus, just like in the textbooks, but moving about. 'It's already quite developed,' the doctor said, tickling my stomach with his moustache. 'We'll soon know whether it's a boy or a girl.' Then he lifted his head, took the hood off, looked at me searchingly and said, 'If it's a boy, you will have him circumcized?' As if I had been caught out in something, I blushed, and he, without waiting for a reply, began to ask all kinds of questions: why had I come to the Pitié, why wasn't my daughter with me, I kept trying to explain, but he kept interrupting me, why is your husband not with you, I cried out that he was away on business and anyway he didn't know I was expecting another child. The doctor then looked at me knowingly, and suddenly the dream turned into a ghastly nightmare. I realized that this man was accusing me of having deceived my husband with a German and had decided that this child – not 'another child' as I had said, but 'another man's child' – did not have the right to live. 'No pity for traitors!' he was shouting, leaping round the room like a rabbit and doing a military salute. 'No pity. *Pas de pitié!*' I screamed that it wasn't true, that I was going to tell my husband all about it as soon as he got home, but the doctor was laughing now, he didn't believe me, 'women, they're all the same,' he kept repeating, 'they're all the same. Men are so unsuspecting, I'll talk to your husband, you'll see.' Then he took out of his white coat a huge fob-watch and started to blow it up like a beach ball, terrified, I got off the couch and ran away, half-dressed, out of the hospital, I must have looked crazy, I had to find Robert before this madman could pour out his horrible lies, if he got to him first, Robert would not believe me, I made it to the house, but I had left my bag behind, my bag with my keys, I was oozing sweat, tears and blood, there was blood pouring from between my legs, and I couldn't get into the house.

I had forgotten how fragile and ready to fall apart it makes you, to be expecting a baby. The nightmare threw me into a terrible state, I woke up in tears, I wanted so much to be able to speak to Robert. Yesterday when he phoned, I could find nothing to say. As if not being able to talk about the one thing I care about had made any other words pointless or futile. Robert thought I was not interested in what he was saying, he must have been depressed about problems with his work, and in no time the conversation became acrimonious, he began to shout, I began to cry, it was ludicrous. When he realized I was crying, he apologized. Robert is not unkind, and we still love each other. Why does happiness always seem to pass us by, without our being able to enjoy it? It must have been this stupid quarrel that poisoned my dream. I am trying to forget the end, and just to remember the beginning, the image of the baby. My baby. Will it be a girl or a boy? We'll soon find out, the dream-doctor said. But in real life I will have to wait some months yet.

Monday 25 January

I slept badly again. Because of the bad dream the night before, I suppose. And, I don't know why, I was worrying about how Robert will react. How will he greet this child? He's very fond of Colette and, when he has the time, he is a good father. It's true too, that when we got married he wanted plenty of children. At least three or four, he used to say. But, try as I might to reassure myself, I couldn't get to sleep.

This morning I feel tired, but calmer. These panic attacks are ridiculous. Probably it's just that I am alone too much. How can you enjoy a treasured secret that you can't share with anyone? Robert will be home tomorrow. This hell is coming to an end. I asked Mme Nourricier if she can keep Colette for the evening. That way we shall be alone for supper, and we can get used to each other again.

I feel scared, like a new bride.

Thursday 28 January

The last three days have worn me out, drained me completely. I
need to sort out my thoughts and no one can help me. Robert
has become a sort of stranger, an unhappy enemy, taking refuge
in not speaking, my diary is the only place I can turn. Like a
mirror, it helps me to reflect. What kind of a world is it if a
woman who loves her husband can no longer even bear his
child?

On Tuesday, as agreed, I left Colette with Mme Nourricier.
That was my first mistake. When Robert got home, his first
words were for her.

'I haven't seen her for three days and the best thing you can
think of is to leave her with the babysitter for the evening!'

My behaviour was obviously impossible to understand. But I
tried to tell him, I need to be alone with you a little, to be able
to talk, I've got things to tell you, but I'm not flirtatious enough
to play that kind of game, and anyway Robert doesn't like
coquettishness.

'I can't see why you couldn't talk to me with her here. Go on,
call Madame Nourricier and say I'm coming over to fetch her.'

'What, now? You don't want to wait a little?'

'I can't see what difference it would make.'

I don't know why Robert was in such a bad temper. Normally he is calm and easy-going, but that evening he seemed very tense.

'Are you sure everything's all right?'

He shrugged his shoulders.

'Well, are you going to call her?'

Any attempt to get close to him or start a conversation seemed to exasperate him. Worn out, on the verge of tears, I telephoned Mme Nourricier. Robert went to fetch Colette. It was almost nine o'clock when they got home. I was in despair and just wanted to go to bed.

But when they came in, the mood lightened. Father and daughter, glad to be together again, showed how happy they were. Robert told jokes and stories, Colette went into peals of laughter and asked for more. Watching them, I felt hope return. Yes, Robert really did love children. He would be glad to learn I was expecting another.

At last Colette was in bed. She insisted that Robert come and tell her one last story before the light went out. He came back and slumped down on the sofa in the sitting-room.

'So, you had something to tell me?'

I had not imagined it happening this way. I would have preferred to be more in control, to bring the news in after working my way round to it, putting it into a proper perspective. It was so awkward being asked to reply, there and then, to a point-blank question. No, I didn't have 'something' to 'tell' him. it wasn't a thing but a person, an event that I had to share with him, and he wasn't ready for it. I had imagined an intimate conversation, being together again meant just that to me, using our own familiar words to restore what holds us together, to recreate the beginnings of a future in this world which is cutting us off from real life.

Since I said nothing, Robert stood up.

'If you're going to sulk, that's too bad, I'm too tired to argue tonight.'

I shouldn't have started crying, it was the last thing I should have done. Tears make men feel guilty, nothing exasperates them more. But I was too fragile, too bruised, too lonely to hold back the sobs.

'Honestly, Hannah, I don't understand what the matter is with you these days. I can't say a thing without you turning the taps on.'

'Turning the taps on': the words echoed in my ears like an insult. Why was he trying to hurt me? Robert knows that I hate vulgar expressions, in the past we used to share this distaste, now what was happening to him? A few years ago, I would probably have pleaded with him, Robert, please, listen to me, but I didn't have the strength now, as if my love itself had aged. As I have grown older, I have become prouder, the world we are living in makes it necessary, the soft-hearted don't survive long, or else have to barricade themselves in. Now I could hear water running in the bathroom, he was taking a shower, I ought to calm down, go back to him and talk to him.

I truly believe I tried everything. But the world sometimes turns against you, events get out of hand, or people don't hear what you say. That night I undressed, got into bed with a book and waited for Robert to come and join me. When he came into the bedroom in his pyjamas, I tried to catch his eye, but he went straight to his suitcase and began unpacking. I put down the book. The whole night lay ahead. Suddenly I was filled with an infinite spirit of patience. I had a vital piece of news to tell him, it concerned him closely, it mattered to our shared life, and somehow I would have to manage it.

Waiting for him to finish, I watched him come and go in the room. His drawn features made him look older, nearer forty. Had this mission gone as planned? He has spoken very little to me about his work and not at all about his unofficial activities. But I have always trusted him. Robert is a serious man, a conscientious man, someone you can count on. I knew he had contacted the Resistance, he told me so because he thought I ought to know the truth about that, but made me promise never to ask him questions about it.

'Our silence is our protection, do you understand?'

I had agreed. I was proud of him. Now I was starting to wonder whether this silence between us, this silence which was gaining ground, might not end up driving us apart.

When he had finished, he slipped into bed, switched off the

lamp on his side, gave me a quick kiss on the forehead and turned his back on me. I was too slow, didn't manage to react fast enough. Our talk would have to be put off till the next day. I turned off my light too. My eyes hurt and I felt sick. I waited a few moments in the dark, then in the familiar warmth I moved closer to him, put my arm round his waist and pressed my whole body against him, as if to merge with him. He didn't say anything or move, but I felt him relax gradually and start to breathe more deeply. I pressed my stomach more closely against his back, as if to make him feel what I had been unable to say, because I had felt that he was unready to receive this news, which ought to have been easy to communicate without words, since it was a joy to be shared, love, the future. We were going to have a child, the very words brought tears to my eyes, it must be a joy, the idea that it could be anything else was unbearable.

The next day everything happened very fast. Robert came into breakfast looking rested and relaxed, and suggested calling at my office to take me out to lunch. I accepted. The morning was so busy that I didn't have time to think, and by one o'clock I had broken the news to him.

At first he didn't react at all. Then after a silence he asked:

'So what are you going to do?'

I replied that I had been to see Dr Lebrun and that he had agreed to take me on as his patient.

'Oh come on, Hannah, you surely don't imagine that we can keep this child?'

I shall remember that sentence all my life. 'You surely don't imagine...' My mother, with her pursed lips and her tight skirts might have said something like that: 'My dear little girl, you surely don't imagine that women are meant to be happy.' Yes, that is exactly what I did imagine. It was all of a piece with my faith in life. Not some naïve or natural faith, some obscure force, curled up inside me and preventing me from having any absolute belief. But I wanted to be able to believe in life, to have the right. And this child, yes, I could imagine that too, perfectly well, in fact. I had already seen it in my dream. And anyway I wasn't merely imagining it; it really did exist, the doctor had felt it and so had I that night, for the first time.

'But Hannah, this is madness. There's a war on.'

For goodness sake, did he think I didn't know that? Was life going to stop because of it ? But Robert insisted.

'I'll call Lebrun and talk to him about it. It's impossible.'

'Don't you love me any more?'

'Now you're being stupid. Or just not thinking. Of course I love you, but you don't appreciate how serious things are. At any moment we may have to leave France, cross the frontier, find new lodgings, new work. How will we manage all that if you're pregnant, or with a babe in arms? We already have to worry about Colette. No, listen, it's impossible.'

I can hear Robert's voice but I'm not listening any more, I can't understand what he is saying, or rather I understand that he doesn't want this child I'm carrying, our child.

'How far gone are you?'

'I'm not quite sure, getting on for four months I think, because I've felt it move.'

Robert went pale, and asked me for the doctor's phone number.

'There's no time to lose,' he said before going off to phone.

No time to lose. He talks about us as if we were a problem to be solved. This is a nightmare. He came back smiling, for the first time, but I would have preferred never to have seen that smile.

'He'll see us right away.'

I allowed myself to be pushed around like a doll, I was no longer there, he put me in a taxi and we found ourselves in the surgery.

'Four months is very risky,' the doctor said quietly.

But Robert had decided, he would pay whatever it took, he would take all the medical precautions necessary, he simply asked Lebrun to tell him who would do the abortion.

'You'll have to go to Geneva.'

In three days it was all fixed, the appointment had been booked, the frontier passes obtained, the hotel room and the train ticket reserved, and it was arranged that Colette would stay with Mme Nourricier while we were away.

'I'm coming with you.'

I didn't protest. What does it matter? Robert knows me, he

knows that I will not keep this child against his will. But he's conscientious. He has decided that at such a difficult time for me, his place is at my side.

Wednesday 3 February

A girl, oh God, it was a little girl. I think that if I hadn't known, or if they hadn't told me, it might not have hurt so much. I would have preferred this baby to be somehow abstract, a baby with no sex, no future. But knowing that it's a little girl, that it *was* a little girl, gives her a reality that makes the loss even harder to bear.

Apart from that, everything went smoothly. For the doctor, at any rate: mother alive, baby dead, that's what he was asked for, after all, he's kept his side of the contract. Robert paid — I've no idea how much it cost, a fortune probably, I don't want to know. The idea that murder could have a price makes the world a dreadful place to me.

Robert is being kind, considerate, attentive. Now that everything has gone according to plan (his plan), he doesn't miss any opportunity to try to please me.

Not that there's any point.

Nothing can bring me any pleasure now.

Friday 5 February

A little girl. I can't get that idea out of my head.

We are back home, life goes on, Robert goes to work, so do I, and Colette is at Mme Nourricier's all day. I feel very low, but Dr Lebrun says that's normal. He says it will take some time to get over it. He suggested sending me on sick leave and advised me to spend a few days in the country. The country! Why not Switzerland while he's at it? After all, he knows some good addresses there...

Friday 12 February

Robert has not mentioned our leaving town again. And I don't dare ask him. What if he made up this story of having to leave, just to persuade me into it?

I mustn't let myself be blinded by the pain, or let it turn into bitterness. Robert has always behaved perfectly, what I mean is, he has acted more generously to me than many men would have in his place. He left Brussels, he went into exile, and all to protect me. He even managed to get us both baptized, Colette and me, and invented an identity for me, from somewhere in the French provinces, which will keep me safe from detection. Was he afraid that this new baby would bring the whole thing tumbling down? Robert, Anne and Colette Périer: we're a Franco-Belgian family now, nothing suspicious about us. What was he afraid of? Of course I have had to give up my real name in public: Hannah sounded a bit suspect. And my parents. And my sister. Where are they now? I haven't had any news for six months. All the terrible things one hears. Who is one to believe? I don't even dare talk about it to Robert. What sort of a world are we living in, if words exchanged in our own home can become witnesses for the prosecution? If men can voluntarily turn into the butchers of their own children?

Friday 19 February

Yesterday Léonore was arrested. It happened at lunchtime. Two policemen were waiting outside for her. She didn't come back all afternoon. At about five o'clock M. Thibaut came into the office and started looking through her desk. In the end he took out a thick file of papers and asked me to deal with it.

'These are the complaints from last month,' he said. 'We mustn't get too far behind.'

Does he think she's not coming back, then? His face remained quite inscrutable. Elizabeth and I exchanged a glance, no more. Everyone thinks the same thing, but to say it out loud would give it a reality none of us wants to believe in.

Tuesday 23 February

Léonore isn't coming back. Yesterday we kept expecting her in vain: every time the office door opened, Elizabeth and I would both look up, with the same hope, but the day ended without any more news. Then this morning M. Thibaut brought a young woman into the office.

'Mademoiselle Renaud will be replacing Madame Jakob while she's away,' was all he said.

Jakob. Leonore had always told us that her family was Alsatian, going back generations, so she wasn't afraid of anything.

'We've less to fear than anyone else,' she would laugh. 'Alsatian is practically the same thing as German, after all.'

My brain feels as if it is being poisoned every day: this poison will drive us mad, perhaps it will make us as brutal as our enemies. At home, before the war, we never spoke about our Jewish origins. I learnt I was Jewish just when I had to start keeping quiet about it:

'I'll tell you the truth, but keep it a secret. Your life could be in danger.'

What insanity. Besides, my father is Belgian, and Mother, whose family was Hungarian, wasn't even brought up in the Jewish faith. Our only tradition at home was joking. Is it our laughter they want to kill?

Friday 26 February

Since getting back from Geneva, I've been sleeping badly. Yesterday I thought for a moment of calling Dr Lebrun, then I didn't. I don't want to see him again. His reassuring words make me feel murderous. Why did he go along so willingly with Robert's suggestion? I can't get rid of the idea that if it hadn't been for him, for his cowardly, guilty agreement, I would still be carrying my child. Another week or two and Robert would have given in, because the operation would have been too dangerous to put me through.

Saturday 3 April

Last night I didn't get to sleep until two in the morning. In the end, when I did fall asleep, I had a dream that has been haunting me all day, with its images and even its sensations.

I dreamt I was about to give birth. Actually at first I went to the hospital for something quite different: I had caught my finger in a door, the middle finger of my right hand: the tip had gone blue and I could hardly feel it. My mother was saying, 'You really must go to hospital,' and I realized that the loss of feeling could mean gangrene, if I didn't take care it might have to be amputated, so I did as she said. Once I got to hospital, I found I was very pregnant, the finger was forgotten and the doctor asked me to sit down to be examined and to find out how far the labour was advanced. I was wearing a summer dress, very pale yellow, almost white. The doctor told me to move forward on the chair and put my legs apart; I thought it was odd that he was doing this internal examination in a room where other people were walking about, but since nobody seemed to pay much attention, I told myself this must be usual, and stopped feeling embarrassed. The only thing that bothered me vaguely was that Colette was there, sitting a little way off, while seeming unconcerned, as little children do, she was trying to look under

21

my skirt as the doctor was examining me. The examination itself was conducted oddly: to find out whether the neck of the womb was dilated and if so by how much, the doctor inserted a sort of tube, made of black rubber and very long and thin, I wondered how that was going to get into the womb, and when he pulled it out the tube had swollen and changed colour, now it was orangey-red, and the doctor was nodding his head approvingly; yes the tube had almost doubled in size, that meant the neck of the womb was dilated (I gathered the tube had reached inside and touched the baby, and indeed I thought the change in colour must be the result of the contact), so I had not come to the hospital too soon at all, I would have to stay there, because I was about to give birth.

When the doctor went away, I stayed sitting on the chair, with no willpower left at all. There flooded through me a strong and contradictory urge, both sweet and powerful, comfortable yet overwhelming. I wanted to cry and cry, and could feel this little girl – because I knew it was a little girl – this child, who was gently pushing her way into the world, as if she were afraid of causing me pain, as if she were taking infinite, delicate trouble to be accepted, and now I was crying, for joy, of course, a rain of warm tears poured down my face, a child is a joy, oh God, how much I loved her already. My mother was standing beside my chair, slightly behind me, I could feel her presence, I needed her.

I woke up to find my face quite dry, I was astonished by this extraordinary dryness, I could still feel on my cheeks the warmth and wetness of my tears, and in my womb an un-fathomable sadness.

I write for only one reason: to get back in touch with myself. To try to recapture what I lose during the night, a world that comes back in memory in the morning, full, whole and present, whereas the world of the day before seems ever more fragmented, blood-spattered, marked by one betrayal after another.

I've always been a rather happy person by nature. In the old days, if I was sad, or even a little less cheerful than usual, Robert would look worried and ask questions and not leave me alone until he could make me smile again. Now he looks away. Is it just because we are surrounded by horrors? Or is it that he knows the real reason for my sadness, and knows that it has to do with him?

Léonore will not be coming back. Elizabeth heard from one of her neighbours that the whole family has been sent to Germany. Where? Who knows? Would it make any difference? The whole of Germany has become a sort of chasm, a black hole beyond the Rhine, swallowing up our people in trainloads, like the ogres in my storybooks.

But Germany is not just transporting victims across the frontier, it is killing them on this side of the border, too, its murderous ideas are poisoning our minds, and the little girl I have lost, the little girl that her father and I have deliberately killed, that little girl, who still haunts my dreams at night, is a victim of this sordid war.

But nobody will ever mention her. I am the only one who will be able to remember her.

Sunday 25 April

Yesterday I went to fetch Colette a little earlier than usual and Mme Nourricier asked me in. 'Come in, I've got a surprise for you.'

She had a mysterious look of a grandmother who is about to spoil a grandchild.

'Would you like a hot drink?'

Five minutes later she brought me a cup of ... real coffee! A cousin had given it to her, he'd got it on the black market.

'That's what he said anyway,' the woman said with a wink. 'He could have got it from the back end of a German and I'd still have drunk it. Ah, coffee! I'd forgotten how good it is!'

Then she began chatting about her neighbours, the woman on the first floor who has German visitors, the man on the third floor who never gets in before eleven at night, and the concierge next door, whose husband has dealings with the Kommandatur. She knows everything and what she doesn't know she makes up. Just as I was getting ready to go, she added:

'And I'll tell you something really funny. You remember that girl up on the third floor, left, the one who was expecting? Well, she's had the baby now, a girl, and what do you think she's called her? Lobelia, if you please. I ask you, why not Anemone or Rhododendron?'

She was laughing but her voice faded away, I couldn't hear her, I felt myself fainting. When I came round, I was on the couch in the sitting-room, with Mme Nourricier patting my cheeks.

'It must have been the coffee. That's what it is. We're not used to it any more, are we?'

Colette at the other end of the couch was looking at me with big eyes.

'You're not pregnant, are you? You're very pale,' said Mme Nourricier.

I wanted to be sick, but above all to get away, to escape from this woman who never stops talking, to get away from her world where the talk is all about pregnancy, babies, names.

Monday 3 May

Sometimes I feel guilty for speaking about Germany the way I do. How many Germans are suffering from Nazism today, even more than we are? More, because the monsters who govern them are their brothers, that is just the worst of it, and kinship seals their lips. It's easy to point to the enemy over the frontier. It's easy to accuse others, foreigners, of causing one's unhappiness. But to realize that the evil is at home, among those who live in the same country as you, speak the same language, are born of the same blood, to stand up to that evil in yourself and denounce it, that is the most difficult thing of all. 'To stamp out the evil in your own backyard.'

Tuesday 4 May

Sorting through some papers, I came across a newspaper cutting from last year:

FROM 7 JUNE
THE YELLOW STAR MUST BE WORN BY ALL JEWS
over the age of six
It will be worn on the left side of the chest

The official journal containing the ordinances of the Militaerbefehlshaber in Frankreich has published the following regulation:

By virtue of the full authority vested in me by the Führer and Oberster Befehlsfaber der Wehrmacht, I order as follows:

I. Distinctive sign to be worn by Jews.

1. It is forbidden for any Jew aged six years or more to appear in public without wearing the Jewish star,

2. The Jewish star is a six-pointed star, about the size of the palm of the hand, with a black outline. It is made of yellow fabric and carries in black letters the inscription 'Juif' [Jew]. It must be worn in a clearly visible position on the left side of the chest and must be firmly sewn on the garment.

II Penalties

Any infringement of the present ordinance will be punished by imprisonment and a fine, or one or other of these penalties. Police measures, such as internment in a camp for Jews, may be added to or substituted for these penalties.

III Date of application

The present ordinance will come into force 7 June 1942.
    Der Militaerbefehlshaber in Frankreich

Below and to the right, two inserts complete the information. The first, bearing the title SPECIAL NOTICE, carries the following details:

All Jews obliged to wear a distinctive sign by virtue of the 8th ordinance of 29 May 1942 concerning measures taken against Jews, must report to the police station or sub-prefecture nearest their home to collect badges in the form of a star, as outlined in the first paragraph of the ordinance. Each Jew will receive three badges and will in return have to give in one coupon from his clothes ration.
    Signed: *The Chief of Police and SS, attached to the Militaerbefehlshaber in France.*

The second notice, in bureaucratic vein, sets out the practical arrangements for this crime under the heading DISTRIBUTION OF SPECIAL BADGES TO JEWS.

So as to conform to the above ordinance, all Jews male and female under instructions to wear the special badge must collect it from the police station in their district or ward on the dates and in the order prescribed below:
    Surnames beginning with A and B: Tuesday 2 June
    C to G inclusive: Wednesday 3 June
    H to L inclusive: Thursday 4 June
    M to R inclusive: Friday 5 June
    S to Z inclusive: Saturday 6 June

Identity cards and clothing coupons must be presented.

Any persons failing to attend on the prescribed date will be liable to penalties laid down in the ordinance.

All Jews to whom this measure applies must be in possession of their badges by 6 June at the latest.

I read and re-read these astounding lines, which remind me that for over a year now I have been living in illegality and in betrayal of my family, and try to convince myself that Robert was right to invent a new identity for me.

And I cannot manage it.

Wednesday 5 May

A new page each new day. As if every time I return to this journal I am somehow hoping to start from scratch.

Friday 7 May

Tonight we celebrated Colette's fourth birthday. Robert somehow found a chicken and I concocted an apple cake, and we invited the Bertrands round to share our meal. It was a nice evening. Their daughter Catherine had drawn a picture of a Christmas tree with four candles on it for Colette.

'Whenever there's a party she thinks it's Christmas,' her mother explained.

Catherine is six. Colette had been given a packet of sweets by Mme Nourricier and we gave her a china doll in a white lace dress and shiny shoes. When I asked her what she was going to call it, she looked me straight in the eyes, was silent for a moment, then said;

'I don't know, I'll have to think.'

After the meal, we drank a toast to the end of the war, without much faith. Joel chose a moment when the children were playing in the bedroom to tell us that they are leaving Paris next week, going south to be with his family.

'At least down there they don't have all these food shortages.'

I glanced at Robert, but he didn't react. He simply said when they left:

'Send us your address, won't you? After all you never know.'

Sunday 13 June

Robert is away on another business trip, for a week. He has promised to call me every night. By the way he said, 'Don't worry,' I knew he was not going for the firm. Why does he keep me at arm's length about his political activities? If they arrested him, they'd arrest me too, anyway. The police would never believe that I knew nothing about it. When he gets back, I mean to speak to him.

Tuesday 15 June

Since Robert left, I've been sleeping like a baby, and, not only that, I have extraordinary dreams that carry on from one night to the next. This hasn't happened to me since I was a child. It's rather nice: I feel as though I am a spectator of another life that belongs to me, too, a life in which there are no obstacles to my wishes. I suppose drugs must have a similar effect.

It began the night he left. This time I dreamt that I was giving birth. I was back in the same hospital as in my last dream, I had been taken into a private room and, with my mother at my side, I was giving birth to a little girl.

'What are you going to call her?' my mother asked.

I can still hear myself reply, echoing the words of my own daughter.

'I don't know, I'll have to think.'

At this, my mother took out of her bag a packet which she handed to me. I opened it and found some beautiful shiny slippers and a man's necktie.

'The tie is for her future husband,' my mother explained. 'You know it is a tradition with us. When a girl is born, you always give her a tie. It's a way of wishing her long life and happiness.'

That night, for the first time, Robert appeared in my dream.

'You see, I was right,' he said with a smile.

I understood then that, for him, the trip to Geneva had just been a ruse to trick the Germans and that he had secretly never meant to stop me having the child.

'And besides, you see, I've already had a set of papers made.'

He handed me an identity card, a passport, a frontier pass, all in the name of Louise Périer.

Louise.

Friday 18 June

Between my dreams and reality, I am leading a double life. I go to bed as if to work, when the work in question restores one to life. At the office I've got my second wind now, and I handle all the difficult files so quickly that M. Thibaut has given me other assignments that have been pending. He has hinted I might even get a pay rise if I carry on like this. The suggestion, which would once have cheered me up and made my heart beat faster, now seems almost comical and I received it with a lightheartedness I would not have suspected in myself. Is it that I don't care? Not exactly. It just means less than it once would have; my work has less place in my life, as if my real interests were now elsewhere. How can I put it? Perhaps I am simply happy. These dreams reconcile me to myself and bring me a feeling of peacefulness such as I have not known for a long time. Perhaps there is something a little crazy about it. But I don't want to ask myself that just yet. I don't want to disturb this feeling of happiness which is as strange as it is unhoped-for. Who knows how long it will last anyway? For three nights now, I have been breastfeeding Louise. She looks at me with her china-blue eyes, she seems happy, and last night I dreamed of her laugh, and laughed with her. I woke with the impression

that she had come back and that I would never lose her now.
    Robert will be home tomorrow.

Tuesday 22 June

Two days with a high fever have left me exhausted, aching all over as if I had been beaten. This morning I got up for the first time, but I felt dizzy and had to go straight back to bed to drink an infusion I'd made myself. Is it flu? Probably, some virus going the rounds, because when I telephoned the office and spoke to Elizabeth yesterday, she told me that the new secretary has the same thing.

It started the night after Robert came home. At the time, he didn't believe me, interpreting my headache as an excuse to reject him. But when I took my temperature and he saw it was over 39°, he calmed down and became kind and caring. He is taking Colette to Mme Nourricier and fetching her home.

Colette. I have been feeling guilty about her lately. I've been neglecting her, only caring for her automatically, without really looking at her or listening to her. What goes on inside that little head? If I ask myself this, it's because of what happened the other night, which left me with an uneasy feeling that I can't explain. It was the night Robert got home. We had just had supper. Robert was in Colette's room telling her one last bedtime story before putting out the light, and I was reading a book in the sitting-room, waiting for him to come back, when he suddenly came into the room and said:

'Have you seen Louise?'

It was as if I had been struck by lightning, a feeling that something literally cracked in my neck. Since I just looked at him, in a daze, he repeated the question:

'Louise, Colette's doll, have you seen her anywhere?'

I must have gone white, because he came closer.

'Are you all right?'

I said, yes, of course, and, no, I hadn't seen the doll, perhaps Colette had left it in the kitchen. He went out again, and I took a deep breath, my hands and legs were trembling. Was I really going mad? I tried to remember, but no, of course I hadn't told Colette anything about my dream, and the name Louise had never been mentioned between us. Yet how could this simply be a coincidence? I remembered very well on the other hand that, in my dream, I had repeated Colette's exact words when I asked her what she was going to call her doll: 'I don't know, I'll have to think.'

Was it I who had forgotten, then? This was the only plausible explanation. Sometimes in the morning when I am only half-awake, I listen rather absent-mindedly to Colette's chatter, so she could well have told me her doll's name without my taking it in. So it was quite possible that I had heard the name and unconsciously reproduced it in my dream.

I shall have to be content with this explanation, at all events. But why doesn't it quite satisfy me? Yesterday, I asked Colette when she had decided to call the doll Louise, but she couldn't tell me. First of all she said, 'Straight away,' but that can't be right because I remember her reply at the time, which I had even noted down: 'I'll have to think.' So, stupidly, driven by this rage to understand, I pressed her.

'Don't you remember, you said you didn't know, that you would have to think about it.'

She looked at me as if she didn't know what I wanted her to say.

'Well, it was just now, then,' she said in a very small voice.

At the time, her failure to understand enraged me, I flew into a temper and I believe I even shouted at her: 'Oh come on, think!' and she began to cry. Robert came into the room, she rushed into his arms and without a word he kissed her and took her off, leaving me alone.

I'm in the wrong, of course. Colette is too little, she was only trying to please me with her answer. What can be happening to me, if I can no longer hear what my own daughter is saying to me?

Wednesday 23 June

Yesterday I slept all afternoon, without dreaming this time. I feel better today, the fever has gone down and I shall go back to work tomorrow.

I think I have been worrying about nothing. These dreams were probably a sort of rite of passage, a necessary return to an event that was too painful to bear. Now I feel sure I shall forget it all and return to normal. I have decided to talk to Robert about his political activity and offer to help. If the family is to be at risk anyway, better that both of us should be involved. At least while we are undiscovered, we will be doubly effective.

I have also decided to spend more time with Colette, take more trouble with her, talk more to her. She is growing up and changing, and if I carry on like this, she will be married before I know what is happening.

Sunday 27 June

At last I have had it out with Robert. At first he wouldn't listen. He didn't want me to be involved in any secret activity and refused even to consider that I should take any risks. But when I argued my point – basically that he is putting me at risk in any case – he gave in and agreed to give me some little things to do from time to time.

'"Little things" is a figure of speech,' he said. 'You know that in this struggle everything counts. The least little thing.'

I know he was not saying that just to flatter me, and he's right.

When he said this, my heart leapt for joy. Should I dare to tell him that? Not so much for political reasons but because of the happiness of being back in touch with him, being able to help him and draw us closer together in some shared activity. In any case, I find it hard to believe in the victory of good over evil or of the rule of law over brute force. I want to believe only what I can see, not what I might hope for if I were blind.

In the end, I am making this commitment for selfish reasons: because whatever happens, whatever has already happened, I don't want Robert ever to forget how much I love him.

1947

Thursday 27 March

It is four years now since I wrote anything down in this diary. Four years that seem to have gone past in a flash. I can still see myself writing the last words, 'how much I love him', I was wearing a tailored suit and sitting on the sofa in the flat in the rue Montorgueil. Just at that moment, Robert came in and kissed me, as if he had heard me and was answering me. And yet how much has happened since that day, 27 June 1943. I leave it to the historians to sort out what happened in world history. What I have lived through myself and still am living through has been enough to plunge me into a confusion from which the only escape may be to write things down in this diary.

First of.all, I have my own name back, that is, my given name. I am no longer Anne, that monosyllabic false identity – it may have saved my life, but I felt cramped in it. I've recovered my palindromic name, Hannah, and that feels better. I draw from this the strength to bear everything that has happened, the loss of my family: my parents and sister were deported because they had the courage not to cheat about their origins.

Yes, it's true, I feel guilty. But of what? Of lying? Of not having died with them? The hardest thing of all to bear is a feeling I cannot get rid of that these deaths were in vain. The martyrs of

45

the past serve only to feed the hate of the survivors, and to dig the graves of future martyrs, we should be wary of martyred peoples and above all try not to create any. They serve only as excuses for hate, they sustain the vicious circle of history, by allowing the living to lay the blame for their sins on the fathers of their enemies. And we ought to be wary of the churches, too, telling us about hereditary sins to be expiated. The original sin is in the word that encourages the crime. As for those who kill, there is only one possible attenuating circumstance: when they are sick. But they have no excuse.

Since the Liberation we have been living in a little three-room flat in the rue de Vaugirard near the Saint-Placide cross-roads in Montparnasse. I have a new job that interests me, in a pathology lab. Colette goes to the local school. She is seven now, nearly eight, a dreamy child with moments of gaiety. Over the last two years she has become very keen on painting. Although she seems to me to be very gifted, I try not to treat her as child prodigy. She is still as fond as ever of Robert, and he returns her affection in full.

Robert. It's about him that I must speak, my heart's concern, the centre of my life, my joy and my suffering, and I feel lost. The Resistance brought us together, it is true. Working alongside him for the cause made me able to enjoy the victory as a shared triumph. I was proud not only of him, I was proud of both of us, and he shared, and still does share, this feeling. But alongside this story, which will be the stuff of family myth and which we will one day tell our grandchildren by the fire, there are other stories, secret and hidden stories that we don't tell, the ones we cannot speak of, the ones we can't share, stories that separate us.

The main one is this: Robert has been unfaithful to me. It has been going on for three years now.

I took six months to notice. His mistress was a young woman in our network, whom I knew slightly. I told myself that she must have been dazzled by the exploits of this young Resistance leader and I tried to treat the affair lightly as a passing fancy; since I was sharing Robert's work, I felt I was in control and above jealousy. It was the time for grand causes. Did Robert realize that I knew? If so, he must have thought that I was able to deal with it. I gave no sign of knowing. Making a scene would have seemed undignified. Or else I would have had to make up my mind to leave him. And that was out of the question. I loved him (I still love him) and continued to have complete confidence in him; when I say in him, I mean in his love and esteem for me, as well as in his sense of duty, and no silly affair or even a youthful infatuation would change my mind. But why was he unfaithful to me? I supposed that he had been seduced by Françoise's charm – she has enough and to spare, and I could recognize that. I also told myself that the death of Louise, that murder we shared but which was more his responsibility than mine, had removed the original innocence from our relationship, had taken away some lightness of being, so that he needed to look elsewhere, if only for the illusion of that innocence. In short, I found plenty of excuses and explanations to redeem him in my own eyes. I also thought that Françoise's charm would have the usual life-span of the love-philtre, that the effect would wear off with time, that we were living through an extraordinarily troubled age, and that these things would not last either. We were beginning to believe more and more firmly that the war would soon be over and, in my mind, the end of the war would bring the end of this episode. I had very quickly seized on this idea and clung to it. Life had only to return to normal for Robert to return to me. Above all, I had not lost the hope, or rather the intention, once peace returned, of having another child.

After the euphoria of the Liberation and all the handing out of medals for heroism, Robert went through a serious crisis: his former work didn't interest him any more, the Resistance had made him more aware of history and current affairs, and he decided to become a journalist. I entirely approved of the idea. Robert has always combined great steadiness of character with a sense of observation and analysis which would certainly bring him success in journalism. He was surprised at my reaction.

'I'll have to travel. You'll be left on your own a great deal.'

That didn't frighten me. And in any case, I had no great taste for a shared life if it was likely to seem a prison.

A week later he was taken on, for a trial period, on a major daily paper. I was not at all surprised that it happened so soon: as

France emerged from disaster, everything seemed possible. With his first pay cheque, we celebrated at the Petit Saint-Benoît the beginning of real life. Real life? The week after that, I noticed that Françoise was signing articles in the same paper. So the change of heart had been her idea.

I know that they go on seeing each other, quite openly, since they work in the same office. I know, too, that Françoise is not married, that she sometimes telephones the house, on the pretext that it is about work, and that she never calls on the days Robert is late home. Since I don't know what to do, I say nothing. I am too afraid that if I do speak, the words will spill out faster than my thoughts and destroy everything I hold most dear.

Friday 28 March

I have not yet written down the most important thing. Louise has come back. Or rather, she has not left me. Except for a few intervals which never last more than a month or two, I have been dreaming about her for almost four years.

The disturbing thing is the powerful sense of reality that comes from these dreams. For one thing, she is growing up. I've been dreaming in real time, if I dare call it that, from breastfeeding and the first time she looked around, to the bottle, then to solids, her first smiles, her teething and the tears that went with it, her first steps, her first words. Afterwards, remembering my dream and comparing the dates, I have worked out that each time my dream showed her at the exact age she would have been if she had lived.

There's something else, too: these dreams have a special quality, a clarity – the colours, above all – such as my dreams have never had before. I haven't seen a technicolour film yet, although they are making them now, it seems, but I imagine they must be like what I see every time I find Louise again. It is very beautiful, but terrifying. In the ordinary way, dreams are bearable because of the very strangeness of the images, that distance from reality that allows us to slot them automatically into the memory as a product of the imagination. But these dreams, which have become the setting for Louise's life, these dreams are quite different. Only my reason tells me that they are dreams; my reason can still tell the difference between sleeping and waking. Otherwise, the images that I see are so lifelike, so logically put together, so like the usual representation of the real world, that I feel as though I were watching a play in which some other woman, who simply has the same name, Hannah, is bringing up a little girl called Louise, who will soon be four years old.

Thursday 10 April

One thing that has happened during these silent years is that I have read Freud – well, some of Freud, at any rate. I discovered in these writings perspectives on the human soul that nobody should be in ignorance of today, and they have led me to this idea: that the history we learn at school is to humanity what the family romance is to the neurotic personality – a justification for his folly, his deviant behaviour, his aberrations. I remember my mother bursting out laughing when she discovered in a history book meant for French primary schools that Louis XI was described as a 'great king', and Charles the Bold as 'an ambitious noble'.

'Back home in Belgium' – that was where she was born, her parents were Hungarian immigrants – 'we learnt just the opposite: the "goodie" was Charles the Bold and Louis XI was the "baddie".'

Her remark opened up a chasm at my feet. I was reassured only by her laugh, that laugh I can still hear in my ears, and that I miss so much now, laughter that said, 'Don't worry, the truth exists but it is somewhere else.' Was it for that truth that she died?

Little children should be told first of all the history of their own people, or rather its legends, then when they are about ten, they should be told the same story as seen by others. That way one would learn while very young, and in a convincing way, that there is no such thing as history, only a collection of stories.

Above all, one would learn not to trust political speeches that claim to be based on history instead of on moral values. Hitler would never have come to power if someone had cut out of his speeches all the so-called historical arguments he stuffed them with.

Man's great weakness, and it makes him human and marks him off from the wild beasts, is his guilt, his need to justify his crimes

Pure hatred is not strong enough to sway a crowd; it needs a story, an ideology, a version of history that travesties the cause and claims that black is white.

Love, on the other hand, needs no arguments.

That was what Rousseau meant, I think, when he defended the idea that man was basically good. What he preferred to forget was that man may be good but he is also weak and malleable.

The saddest thing of all is that this sickening war, whose endless horrors are being revealed to us daily now, will not even serve as a terrible lesson. One or two generations, perhaps, will be able to survive by thinking, 'Never again,' sustained by memories of the unbearable. But after that, what will protect us from forgetting and the blind return of the same thing?

Wednesday 23 April

For a week now Robert has been away for the paper, and for a week I have been spending nightly idylls with Louise. I only have to shut my eyes for a few moments before sleep takes over. We are both living in a big house that I do not recognize, one I don't think I have ever seen, a sort of country pavilion with a large stone terrace in front of it, leading to a gravel drive. All round the terrace and alongside the house runs a flowerbed full of brightly coloured dahlias, from white to deep blue, with vivid reds and yellows, and a scattering of softer pastel shades of pink or mauve, protecting our happiness. A little way off a majestic cedar of Lebanon, hundreds of years old – my father tells me it was a tree of Liberty planted by the Revolution – shades a lawn sprinkled with daisies. Downhill from it is a little ornamental pond, in the shape of a square, full of water-lilies that make a sort of pavement for the frogs, and bordered by a narrow band of rose-pink brick.

I have been here with Louise for six nights running. In this great house she has a large bedroom with a parquet floor, its windows looking out to the back over a well-kept kitchen garden. My room is across the corridor from hers, and has a view of the cedar tree. When I lean out and look to the right, I can see the pond.

These nighttime days – in my dreams the sun is always shining – are passed playing, laughing, reading and talking. Louise has become a happy and mischievous little girl, full of health and energy, a chatterbox who likes acting a part. I wonder where she gets this *joie de vivre*, perhaps from me, since when I was little I, too, was carefree, but that is all so far away now. Yet in her company I find occasional moments of happiness, as if she were waking up the Hannah of days gone by, the Hannah my father loved so much, who used to act the fool on starchy family occasions, making everyone laugh and clap. I tell myself that Louise ought to have lessons in dancing, music and drama, that she is a gift from heaven, talented at everything, infinitely talented.

My father has always lived in this big house, taking refuge in a little room in the attic where he spends his time copying out musical scores. My mother and sister have come to join us here. They arrived with masses of luggage in a glossy black sedan. Louise ran out on the path to meet them and they recognized her at once, although they had never seen her before. I put them both in the bedroom next to mine.

We lead a peaceful family life here. My father writes away and comes down every evening between five and six to smoke a pipe on the terrace, looking out at the cedar. My mother takes care of the flowers and cooks spaghetti – she has brought a machine back from Italy so that she can make her own pasta – and my sister Isabelle spends her days praying in the nearby chapel. Since she arrived, she has dressed as a nun, which strikes me as perfectly normal. Indeed that was how I introduced her to Louise: 'This is your aunt Isabelle, my sister in holy orders.'

Thursday 24 April

A seventh night running with Louise. This time, the weather changed. It was the end of the day and clouds were piling up in the sky, it was almost dark, and in the garden my mother was finishing watering the flowers. I was in my room, hanging up some curtains which I had just washed, when I heard my mother calling from a distance. Her voice sounded very small.

'Hannah!' she was calling. 'Hannah, come and see!'

I went to the window, looked for her, and at last I saw her. She was a tiny figure at the foot of the cedar, looking down at the ground as if she were watching something. I shouted and waved, to show I had heard. She raised her head and waved back, pointing to the ground at her feet.

'Come and see!'

I didn't want to go, I wanted to finish what I was doing, but she insisted as one would with a child.

'There are new flowers here, a kind I've never seen, pansies, and masses of marigolds.'

She seemed extraordinarily happy with her discovery.

Going downstairs to meet her, I thought of Colette and Louise, for now Colette was in the house, too, having joined us for the school holidays. That very morning Robert had dropped her off by car before going to work. Colette had also brought a great many suitcases, and her easel and paintbrushes, and Louise had welcomed her so warmly that I felt jealous. I was cross with myself for this unworthy feeling, and in any case it passed quickly when I saw the two sisters set off hand in hand for the garden. I had asked Colette to look after Louise.

'Be careful, she is still only little.'

Colette had nodded to show she understood, then went off, her paintings under her arm, her other hand holding Louise's, and the little one was jumping for joy.

As I went down to meet my mother, I wondered where they had gone, it was a long time since I had seen them, and it looked as if a storm were brewing. I would have to go and look for them, so I hastened my steps to join my mother and ask her to help me find them, but when I got to the cedar tree, I found her covered in blood.

'Look,' she said, showing me a deep cut across her wrist, 'how silly.' Her face was already deathly pale. 'I was cutting a marigold with my secateurs, and the stem was too tough, it wouldn't break and the blade slipped. It's not serious.'

She was saying that to reassure me, but she didn't believe it at all, the blood was gushing from the cut and I saw that if we didn't get help, she might bleed to death. I called my father to help us, but it was not he who came but Colette. Colette without Louise. 'Where's your little sister?' Colette motioned vaguely towards the fishpond, then my father arrived with his walking stick, his pipe in his mouth, smiling. I ran off, certain that something had happened to Louise. I imagined her drowning, green with the mud from the bottom of the pond, her stomach swollen, her eyes dim, I couldn't breathe, I ran and ran, oh God, what a way it was to the pond. I arrived as the last ray of sunlight struck through the clouds. Louise was standing in the pond, with the water coming up to her thighs, holding her skirt up in one hand like a scoop and with the other trying to catch the frogs that hopped from one lily pad to another all round her, as if to mock her. She was laughing, clear peals of laughter, and I saw that she was not really trying to catch them – it was a game, a sort of leapfrog, which the frogs were enjoying, giving this new playmate a display of their acrobatics in a spectacular water-show. Every twist and leap made Louise laugh even more, the boldest frogs leaped over her skirt without falling in, and if by chance one of them was caught, Louise put it on the palm of her hand and held up her arm in the air, like a diving board, so that the frog could jump back to join its friends.

I sat down a few yards away to get my breath and look at her at leisure, taking advantage of this happy sight which only a moment earlier I had been afraid I would never see again. Colette came to join me and told me that my mother was all right, that the bleeding had stopped.

'Grandpa said that he wasn't worried, that Grandma knows all about blood, she can manufacture it – when she had a miscarriage, it was far worse, it was all over the house.'

At the moment she said the word 'miscarriage', a flash of lightning lit up the sky, followed by a deafening clap of thunder. Automatically I shut my eyes and then I heard an inhuman, heart-rending cry. When I opened my eyes and looked at the pond, the waterlilies, vaguely stirred by the movement of the water, were returning to their places, and the frogs, anxious and stupid, were looking at me. What had happened to Louise?

Saturday 3 May

One cannot stop the past coming back. It is there, imprinted in the body even more deeply than in the memory, and the most reasonable man becomes capable of murdering anyone who twists a treacherous knife in these wounds that never heal.

Man's goodness stops where his suffering begins. That shows where its limits are. It is the suffering that ought to be treated gently, delicately, with a sure touch and above all with intelligence. But how? In my optimistic moments I forget that this is a pious wish, and imagine an ideal form of government in which this truth is accepted, and it is forbidden to exercise political power – either executive or legislative – without banishing all arguments based on history. This would not, of course, mean forgetting about history; on the contrary: special committees, made up of retired historians, psychologists, pyschoanalysts, doctors, sociologists, wise men, given life pensions and co-opted by their peers, could debate these attempts to dig up the past, criticizing them in the light of the different versions available, each of which would be scrupulously tested against certain unquestionable values, such as the 1789 Declaration of the Rights of Man. It would not mean choosing one version or another of history, but it would mean respecting the values that

58

are the basis of our civilization: Liberty, Equality and Fraternity would not make a bad starting-point, after all, unless these words are brandished to cover up wickedness. This would be the only allowable procedure for law-making and judging. But the dream soon fades, common sense brings me back to earth. Would all these so-called wise men not be exactly like most ordinary mortals, governed only by their personal interests? One is the same all one's life, in age as in youth: grey beards and wisdom go together only in fairy tales.

Since the bad dream the other night, I cannot get to sleep. Or else I fall into a sort of coma. In the small hours I drop off exhausted and wake up feeling sick and empty. Robert is back, pleased with the report he has written, pleased, too, no doubt by other delights which we do not share. I have just enough strength not to ask myself this question, and after all it is of only secondary importance in the end. For me there is something else now which is all-important: the child I long for without being able to conceive it, except in my imagination, the child who alone could free me from these recurrent dreams which have no more charms for me, the very prospect of them terrifies me, I dread them as if they were forbidden fruit, but I am also beginning to fear for my sanity, they take up so much room in my life that there is less left for Robert and Colette. The other day, Thursday, I think, I was on my way to the office in the car when, all at once, crossing the road ahead of me, I thought I saw Louise. I slammed on the brakes so violently that the car behind almost went into me. When I came to, my heart was pounding and my legs were trembling. Was it a hallucination? Or am I so tired that I fell asleep for a few seconds? I looked around and saw no one else in the street except an elderly blind lady, knocking her white stick on the pavement for someone to help her cross.

Monday 5 May

I love my husband. I love my daughter. But I am not here with them.

Wednesday 7 May

Until last night, I thought I was pregnant again. My period was about ten days overdue, I was about to go for a lab test, before telling Robert, when it arrived after all – then I wept all night. Robert was so taken aback by my tears that in the end I confessed why I was so unhappy, this at least I can talk to him about, I want to have your child, our child, now, right away. He comforted me as one comforts a child, don't worry, it'll be all right, I love you. At the time his words and caresses relieved me, but now I'm not so sure, something must be wrong, something inside must have gone wrong. I don't understand, perhaps I should see a doctor.

Saturday 10 May

I have made an appointment to see a gynaecologist.

Tuesday 20 May

I've just been to the gynaecologist. He says I must have some tests. I've made the hospital appointment and have to see him next week when the results come back.

Monday 26 May

This waiting stops me writing anything.

Thursday 29 May

I can't have any more children.

[End of the first notebook]

65

Sunday 1 June

It's impossible to turn back the clock and start one's life over again; one has to start from what that life has been, and is, and go on, finding inside oneself the necessary silence, the willingness to look forward to the good things in the world, the work to be done, the values to fight for. But what if one falls back into the same blind alleys, comes up against the same obstacles, that was what happened to me more crushingly than ever the other day when Dr Kranz told me that I cannot conceive again. At the time I collapsed, because the world seemed to be collapsing around me, but no, it was not the end of the world, just of my little universe. And yet I already knew what he was going to say, for years now we have taken no special precautions and the evidence should have been blindingly obvious – that is just what it was, I was blinded and could not see what was staring me in the face. Did I not want to see it? Being blinded, I needed to hear, otherwise why would I have consulted him? I needed someone else to tell me this, someone who knew nothing about me or my reasons for asking.

Coming out of the surgery, I went into a café. I don't smoke, but I bought a packet at random, sat down, ordered a whisky, and smoked three cigarettes one after another, lighting each one from the stub of the last. After that, slightly unsteady on my feet, I flagged down a cab and went to Robert's office.

I had never set foot there before. In the foyer I asked the porter to have someone call my husband, then I lit a fourth cigarette and subsided on to a rather dilapidated sofa at the foot of an imposing stone staircase. Robert, finding me in this shattered state, with a cigarette in my hand, did not need to be told that this was an emergency or how desperate I was. With his usual tact and sang-froid, he took immediate steps to get me away from inquisitive eyes, and we went home in silence. In the taxi I tried to explain, to apologize, for this almost scandalous behaviour, so different from my usual self, I was truly ashamed, but the moment I opened my mouth to speak, a wave of sickness came over me. The taxi dropped us in front of a chemist's shop, I was shivering. Robert patiently cleared up the mess and the cabbie drove off muttering. When we got home, Robert, still saying nothing, helped me up to the bedroom and lay down alongside me, taking me in his arms and then, at last, I burst into tears.

I don't know how long I went on weeping. Perhaps an hour. Great long sobs like in my childhood when my sister for some reason wanted to hurt me – to show her power over me, perhaps – and my little world of loved ones collapsed. But now it was different. I was not weeping over the end of a daydream, or out of loneliness, but because I had come up against an immovable obstacle in real life, because I had discovered in myself, in my own body, an obstacle to my longing for a child, my longing as a woman to have a child, which is a desire as strong and as desperate as the desires *of* a child, it is true. The pain and the sorrow were intensified by the knowledge that I, we, Robert and I, had created this obstacle, for Dr Kranz was in no doubt that my sterility was caused by the late abortion we had carried out in 1943. And how could I tell Robert that, how could I tell him without it sounding like a reproach, without this admission making a lasting breach in our relationship? I was alone, alone with Louise, alone with my now impossible longing, alone with my truth, but this truth, too, was not simple, on one hand, 'You have killed me,' and on the other, 'I love you.' 'You have killed me' is an exaggeration, of course, but I did feel almost like that, as if part of me had been cut away, as if some mutilation had thwarted my longing to give life to another, the only act that justified my own life in my own eyes, so that the wall I had come up against was a kind of partial death, if I did not want to die, I would have to find other reasons to live, and I felt unable to do so. It was impossible, of course, to drag Robert into what he, with a man's natural defence mechanism, would secretly have considered a morass of feminine emotions.

In the depths of my despair I could hear a voice telling me all these reasons to say nothing, and my tears flowed the faster.

At last, slowly, I calmed down. Robert was still there, attentive, loving, ready to help. As if the tears had momentarily washed over the ground of my uncertainty and anguish, I eventually managed to tell him about my appointment with Dr Kranz, and to give him the news that had provoked the crisis. He heard it without surprise, had been expecting it, he said. The idea had already occurred to him, but he had preferred to say nothing, waiting for me to raise the question myself.

Then a long silence fell between us. Like a wounded animal that has narrowly escaped being killed. I looked around me to check that the world was still there. The world was still there, yes, but how different from the one I had imagined, the one I had counted on to build my future life.

Around this thwarted longing which had marked me for ever, I would have to rebuild myself. And Robert would have to help me.

I knew too that I could count on him.

I had counted on a new baby to chase Louise away. I had counted on the future to wipe out the past. Now that that strategy was in ruins, I felt I had two choices: to plunge into frantic activity or to look back at myself, to retrace my steps, deliberately this time, to renew acquaintance with myself, and with the old *joie de vivre* which I had rediscovered in my dreams but which, for reasons I could not explain, had escaped me for so long in real life.

As if he had been reading my thoughts, Robert said softly:

'Why don't we go and spend some time back in Belgium?'

I have not been back since the war. Since my parents were

deported, or rather since this news was given to me over the telephone by the voice of some anonymous official, turning it into a meaningless abstraction, I have blanked out the places I grew up in, certain that I would never have the courage to go back there again. Carrying on the tradition of my mother's family, I, too, have become, as a result of this war waged against wandering peoples, a woman from nowhere. How could I rediscover my roots? They are lost in the mists of time and in lands I will probably never see, where in any case the people speak a language I have never learnt.

But it is not so much my roots I would be looking for with Robert, only my memories. The happiest ones. Those which had nourished my will to live.

Monday 1 September

We have been back home a fortnight now. For nearly two months, taking Colette with us, we have been travelling around the country I thought of as mine when I was a child. In a suburb of Brussels I found the little square planted with lime trees, the low houses all round it with their red-brick walls and slate roofs – they always remind me of red-faced workmen with berets gathering for Sunday lunch. Here in the old days were the little shops, the delicatessen, the grocer's, the baker's. Today most of them have closed down, except the grocer's, which now also sells bread and the local papers on weekdays. I stopped to buy apples and a packet of redcaps, awful chewy sweets that I used to love; my grandmother always used to buy a bag of them for me when I came to play cards with her on Sundays. On the Ostend waterfront I found the little bar where Isabelle and I, usually with money taken from my father's trouser pockets, used secretly to buy bags of chips which we covered with mayonnaise and mild mustard. In Bruges I rediscovered the lace-makers, ageless women sitting out on their doorsteps bending over their work, their fingers moving the bobbins so fast that even the quickest eye can't keep up with them, quite unmoved by the noisy admiration of the tourists.

I also rediscovered, more painfully, the house where I grew up, on the Avenue de la Floride in Brussels, with its wrought-iron porch and the little cobbled pathway leading to the garden behind the house. I peeped furtively through the skylight at ground level into the huge kitchen, a semi-basement room where I used to spend most of my time with my mother, linked to the dining room on the ground floor by the dumb-waiter, a machine that fascinated me. But there was no light showing, no one was there. Colette would have liked to ring the bell and visit, but my courage failed me, and we turned back without trying to get in. It must have been there that the Germans came to ring the doorbell, very early one cold morning, probably there that my mother, my sister, my father, watched by neighbours peeping from behind their blinds – one of those neighbours, no doubt, having given them away ... Nobody had told me what happened, but so many stories like that had circulated, merged together and become one story that I felt I knew it, that that story was now mine, ours, that of my whole family, those who were betrayed, those who ran the risk of being betrayed, those who were surprised at dawn, roused from their deepest sleep, halfway through a dream.

Throughout this pilgrimage Colette and Robert were perfect companions, sometimes religiously respecting my silence, sometimes bombarding me with questions, their way of saying that life is not all memories, that it goes on.

They distracted me too; we visited Antwerp and Liège, places I didn't know.

Then we set off home.

Wednesday 10 September

This trip has done me good. Instead of the sterile anguish that comes from not knowing, I have some real images, I know now that reality is always more terrible than the scenarios one invents to hide it, and curiously this discovery has made me feel more calm.

Robert's kindness has helped too. I have realized that whatever happens, we will end our days together. The novelty of this conviction makes me realize in retrospect that I had begun to doubt it, but I am beginning to get acquainted with these doubts and certainties, like Russian dolls, one inside the other, and they unsettle me less than they once did.

In spite of everything, I'm still suffering from insomnia.

Friday 12 September

Why can't I tell Robert about my dreams? Why can't I confess them to him – yes, confess is the word, as if I were committing an offence against him by carrying on thinking about this child that he killed, that we killed. I would like to tell him that I don't blame him, but that would be dishonest, I do blame him, of course, how can I not admit that? But I blame myself just as much, I blame the whole world, I blame the war that stole from us five years of happiness, of youth, of *joie de vivre* and carefree times. I blame life for not being what I was promised, for not being what I thought I saw in my mother's eyes when she read stories aloud to me as a child. But could Robert understand that? No doubt he would only hear in it a reproach, and conclude that I don't love him any more, or that I love him less than in the past. It's true that it is no longer the same love. At twenty I was in love with a romantic figure, a knight in armour, a fairy-tale hero; today I love him just as one loves a fellow human being on this earth, whose imperfections one knows and accepts. How can I get him to see the truth, that because of these imperfections, these failings, my love is actually strengthened? He wouldn't believe me, he would see in this kind of talk an untruth intended to spare his feelings. And yet it is the truth. As if my dream had taken root in reality. It is a painful reality that separates me from myself, a reality that forces me to keep quiet to avoid the misunderstandings which would be sure to invade the space taken up by self-doubt.

And Robert is a man. He has his own self-doubt. His affair with Françoise is, in my eyes, the saddest evidence of that.

Tuesday 23 September

My dreams have changed their setting. Louise is still the main character, but the country house has disappeared, along with the cedar and my parents, the green landscape has been replaced by the plains of the north, by red-brick houses and cobbled streets. Sometimes by the beaches on the North Sea coast. Last night, for instance, we were visiting a house in Knocke-le-Zoute, a huge empty house full of wooden staircases and banisters, it was snowing outside, a great fire was burning in the grate and we decided to go for a ride in a *cuistax* – a sort of go-cart children and adults drive for fun along the dykes that stretch for miles. But when we tried to hire one, I found myself facing a man in uniform who didn't speak French, I couldn't make out what he was saying to me, it was neither Flemish nor German, and I could gather only one thing: he wouldn't take my money, everyone here had gold coins and bank notes made of pieces of cloth with different values according to their shape – squares, circles, stars. I would just have to go to the bank to get some. Disappointed at missing my fun, I tried to explain to him in a sort of garbled French – as if talking pidgin would make it more understandable – that it was Sunday, the banks were sure to be closed, but my money was good, he would have no difficulty changing it the next day himself. Obstinate as a jailer protected by some stupid regulations, the man wouldn't listen to any argument and kept directing me towards an illuminated building a short distance away, with a red and blue sign flashing sluggishly on and off. As I was turning round to explain to Louise what was happening, I saw her a few yards away talking to a young man sitting in a go-cart, she was speaking in the language I couldn't understand, clapping her hands, then pointing at me. The young man looked at me, then held out his hand to Louise to help her to sit down beside him. I went towards them. Louise introduced her companion, his name was Robert, and explained that he had agreed to take her for a ride, that she would be back in a quarter of an hour.

'You can be changing your money in that time.'

Pleased that she had found a solution, I followed her advice and went back along the dyke towards the flashing sign. The building was the largest casino on the coast. Men and women in evening dress were going up and down the great stone staircase, doormen were checking the appearance of new arrivals, and I realized how dirty and shabby I was; unless I could slip in while one of the watchdogs wasn't looking, I would never be allowed in. Robert – my Robert – then came up to me, wearing a white tuxedo, and threw a large black velvet cape over my shoulders to hide my clothes, laughing as he said:

'Come on, don't make a face. Don't you see that all this is just a charade!'

A charade? I didn't know what he meant, but I followed him and found myself in a vast ballroom. At the entrance a woman was issuing tickets. I explained that I didn't want to go in, just to change some money, the man at the go-cart stand had told me this was possible, but by her expression I could tell I had been misinformed, that I was going to be thrown out, in despair, Robert threw up his hands, he could do no more for me. In a second I was outside the doors of the casino, at the top of the steps, and down below I could see only Louise in rags, lost in a crowd of beggars with no eyes holding out their hands towards me.

When I woke up, I remembered the face of the man at the go-cart stand, he was exactly like M. Thibaut, my ex-boss, who – people told me after the war – had been the one who denounced Mme Jakob to the Gestapo.

Sunday 5 October

Since our stay in Belgium, my dreams have changed. Louise has come back into the scenes of my ordinary dreams, the colours and realistic details that I once found so striking have disappeared, she is now part of my usual imaginings. Is this a good sign?

All the same, she is still growing

In the daytime I think about her as a real person, like any other person around me. Her image is just as unclear, but her presence just as definite. Without my consciously thinking about her all the time, she suddenly swims into my head, taking control of my daydreams, as Colette and Robert do at other times. It is just as if I had dropped her off at school in the morning and was going to pick her up later.

Tuesday 7 October

This morning I received this letter:

> Dear Anne,
>
> Yesterday in the metro I thought I saw you in the distance, but my train was pulling out of the station and I couldn't call to you. When I got home, I looked up your address in the phone book so now I can write to you. I'd love to see you again. I live very near you, 3 rue du Regard, telephone Littré 89 22. Would you like to give me a ring? See you soon, I hope.
>
> Elizabeth Gérard

Elizabeth. I lost touch with her early in 1944 when she left M. Thibaut's office. I never knew why she left. Did she hear before I did the rumour that our boss was in touch with the German authorities? It's a curious coincidence that I should dream about M. Thibaut a few days ago, when I haven't thought about him for years, and that Elizabeth should come back into my life.

It is as if the past sweeps back in waves.

I seem to remember that her husband was a prisoner of war. I'm not sure if I've got that right. I'll call her tomorrow.

Thursday 9 October

Elizabeth came to lunch today. Meeting her again was a great pleasure, much more so than I had anticipated. Was it simply because we had both managed to survive that unspeakable war? She is so discreet and reserved that I never really paid much attention to her before. After all, we were just colleagues in the same office and I don't usually mix my working and my private life. She turned out to be a delightful woman. I am touched, too, by her remembering me and by the straightforward way she contacted me. She turned up at the flat with a bunch of anemones and a book for Colette. She remembered I had a little girl.

We talked about the war. Her husband was indeed a prisoner, now released. He came home much thinner and according to her greatly changed. 'He's not the same man.' What an extraordinary thing to say, and what a strange truth to have to live with. To see a man return, the same yet different from the man you had chosen and loved, and to know that you have no choice – unless you are a monster – but to go on living with him for good. She speaks of it with delicacy that makes me like her even more, but I sense that she is finding it difficult to cope with this situation.

'I'm thirty years old and it sometimes feels as if my life is over,' she said.

They have no children. Before the war her husband wanted them, but not now.

They keep a little stationer's and bookshop on the corner of the rue d'Assas and the rue de Rennes, not far from here. I promised to call on her in the shop.

By the end of the meal we were on such good terms that I almost told her about Louise. But at the last minute I had second thoughts. What if she were to think I was crazy? If someone told me a story like this, I think that is what I might conclude. At any rate I would advise her to consult a psychiatrist. Would I be wrong?

Friday 24 October

This morning I took Robert to Le Bourget to catch the plane to England. When I got back, I bumped into Dr Kranz, near my office. He stopped to greet me and as he was asking after my health, a heavy shower of rain came on. We took refuge in a café and he suggested a hot drink to warm me up. We exchanged a few platitudes and just as we were taking our leave, he asked me to have lunch with him on Monday.

'Whatever for?' I said, taken aback at this unexpected and unorthodox invitation.

To which he replied, 'Why ever not?'

Then he laughed.

'You know the Jewish joke?' he said.

'No.'

'A goy says to a Jew, "Why on earth do Jews always reply to one question with another?" And the Jew says, "Why on earth shouldn't they?"'

I laughed too, and for a second wondered whether to follow it up with the one about the strudel, which I always remember when people tell jokes. He took advantage of my hesitation to repeat the invitation. I accepted without thinking, to avoid embarrassment, I suppose, now I'm scared stiff, my heart is pounding, what on earth do I expect from this rendezvous? And above all, what does he want? He knows I'm married, that I have a little girl, does none of that matter? Having arranged to meet, I watched him walk away. He is a tall, slim, elegant man, with his swirling coat and felt trilby his silhouette looked American, like some heart-throb from the movies.

Saturday 25 October

Since our return from Belgium, Colette has been hiding something from me. When she is not at school, she closets herself in her room for the whole afternoon and forbids me to go in. The first few times I said nothing, but yesterday I became rather cross.

'What's all the mystery?'

Surprised by my reaction, Colette put on a mischievous expression which I have never seen on her face before and replied:

'It's a picture, a new one, I'm finishing it for Christmas. It's going to be a present for you.'

I felt terrible and apologized. In a few seconds the roles had been reversed: I was the daughter, she the mother. I'm ashamed of myself.

On Monday I'm due to have lunch with Dr Kranz, and since yesterday I have been acting like a silly girl. I catch myself whistling tunes, looking at my figure in shop windows, and last night I inspected my limited wardrobe, trying on all my clothes to see which would make me look my best. Am I setting out to seduce him? This is ridiculous. In three days Robert will be back, It's ages since I was so anxious for him to return.

Louise is still preoccupying me, and it is becoming an obsession. I don't write about her every day and some days I decide not to write in this diary at all, as if writing about her will only prolong this imaginary existence that so torments me. But she will not leave me alone.

Thinking psychoanalytically, I have asked myself what she must represent. Is she a substitute for me, or for my sister? No. Louise is so different, so much herself, that I cannot get rid of the idea that she is the little girl who would be alive now if we hadn't killed her.

And after all, how can I consider her a figment of my imagination, when I have felt her move in my womb?

Monday 27 October

When I was a little girl, my mother used to say that we all had a guardian angel who watched over us and stopped us doing silly things. Was it the guardian angel who made me run a temperature of 40° last night? I must confess that I was almost relieved this morning to be able to telephone Dr Kranz at his surgery and call off the lunch.

'I'm so sorry, I can't come out, I have a temperature.'

But he is not the sort of man to be put off by a couple of degrees of fever.

'You forget that I am a doctor,' he replied. 'If you will allow me, I'll call round at lunch time to check how you are and examine you.'

Taken aback, I heard myself say, 'But ... but you're a gynaecologist!'

This exchange was so ridiculous – as I realized myself – that the hearty laugh at the other end of the line made it more so. To excuse myself, I gave him the address of the flat and directions to the right landing.

'I'll be there at one.'

In a few minutes I was up, dressed and ready to drive Colette to school, where she will be all day. Then I called the office to say that I would not be in.

'I have a temperature, the doctor's calling at lunchtime.'

This half-truth affords me childish amusement.

At one o'clock there is a ring at the bell. I open the door to Dr Kranz, who comes in carrying several packets.

'This is our lunch. I assumed that since you were unwell, you would not have gone shopping.'

The absurd predictability of this situation is obvious: this man is setting out to seduce me, it is time to make it clear that I can see what he is up to, and put an end to this juvenile behaviour.

Putting the packets on the kitchen table, he looks at me carefully.

'If I'm not mistaken, your temperature has come down.'

Professionally he approaches, feels my forehead, takes my pulse. I start to feel angry. Angry with myself for these silly girlish daydreams, dishonest dreams of some futile happiness to which I have no right and angry at this play-acting. My eyes move from his bow-tie to his smile and stop at his expression, which is strangely calm. Why did he come?

'Shall I write you a prescription?'

I'm tempted to box his ears. I laugh instead, for something to do.

'You bring food for lunch, then you treat this as a doctor's visit. Are you here as my doctor or as a friend?'

'Does one rule out the other?'

Now I understand: it's still a joke from the other day, replying to one question with another. I will have to tell him the one about the strudel some time. Later. This time, I decide to take him on at his own game.

'Don't you think it does?'

He understands and laughs too.

'Don't let's be enemies.'

He begins to unpack the parcels. He has brought two slices of smoked salmon, some prepared salads from a charcuterie, some wholemeal bread and a bottle of Bordeaux. A real feast.

'Shall we eat in the kitchen?'

He anticipates my actions, opens drawers, lays the table, acts as if he were at home.

'Since you are unwell, I'm taking advantage. Now be a good girl and sit down.'

Overwhelmed by all this, I obey. He pours me a glass of wine. We chat about this and that. At three o'clock he looks at his watch and gets up.

'I'll be late for surgery.'

At the door he kisses my hand and smiles.

'Have I your permission to call again?'

Where would I find the strength to say no?

His name is Michel. Michel Kranz.

Thursday 30 October

Now I know why I find Elizabeth so appealing. She reminds me of my sister Isabelle. There is the same discretion, the same quality of silence. At times, the same smile. Without thinking, I told her this, and saying it suddenly brought tears to my eyes. I surprised myself by this confession, which she greeted with tact and gentleness, putting a hand on my shoulder.

'We can't help it, we are the sacrificed generation. Our mission is not to live, but to remember. For the generations to come.'

I do not believe this kind of nonsense. We will remember, yes, of course, and to our dying day we will be relentlessly pursued by those images of human wickedness. But they will die out with us, and those who come after us will start again from scratch. I don't believe in progress. I would like to, but I can't. If there were such a thing as progress, how could humanity have contrived, after centuries of appalling horrors, to produce a horror greater than anything in the past – the horror of considering and treating human beings as if they were less than human, a herd of evil beasts to be exterminated? Never in history can man have so despised his fellows. Even slaves were better treated. At least they were thought fit to work. How can one section of the human species have come to deem the other section unfit to live? We have come nowhere near expiating this act of insanity. It will leave its traces on all future generations for centuries to come.

Sunday 2 November

The day of the dead. I sometimes envy people who have graves to visit. A grave is a place, like a homeland. Those for whom I am grieving, my family, those closest to me, have no grave. My parents. My sister. Louise. When I am no longer there to remember them, they will not exist for anyone in the world.

Tuesday 4 November

I have never seen so many pregnant women as I have this year whenever I go out in the street, nor so many babies in prams. I thought it must be because I am still so obsessed that I am imagining it, but now the newspapers and the radio have picked up on it, everyone is talking about the 'baby-boom'. France is being reborn, she is bringing children into the world and forgetting the war.

I can't do either of these things, have children or forget the war. Perhaps the two really do go together.

Wednesday 5 November

Why doesn't Michel Kranz telephone?

Thursday 6 November

What if he is waiting for me to make the first move?

No, I must hold out, stick to what he said. What would I look like if I were to call him first?

What I am, I suppose.

Saturday 8 November

Yesterday in the street I saw Robert and Françoise, walking arm in arm and laughing. Just as I was about to cross the road to avoid coming face to face with them, Robert saw me. He dropped her arm, but too late. Our eyes met at a distance, but I did not want her to see me and I walked away fast in the other direction. He stayed with her.

In the evening he came home earlier than usual, with a bunch of marguerites. Was he expecting me to say thank you? As I was arranging them in a vase, Colette took one and began pulling off the petals:

'He loves me, he loves me not, he loves me...'

What got into me? I picked up the flowers, threw them on the floor, fetched my coat and walked out of the house, leaving Robert to clear up the mess.

In the street I started walking. It was cold and the pavements were slippery – there was sleet this afternoon. At the Saint Placide crossroads, I met Elizabeth on her way home with an armful of shopping.

'Why don't you come home with me for a drink?'

I hesitated for a moment, then agreed. She didn't ask me any questions.

When we got there, her husband was sitting at the table in front of a glass of whisky. He offered me some – 'It'll warm you up' – and I took it, then he poured himself another shot. From Elizabeth's expression, I gathered that he was taking advantage of my presence to break the rules.

'Ice?'

Eric, that's his name, has hollow cheeks, a few grey bristles in his straggly moustache, and a receding hairline. His eyes, which are very light blue, almost green, seem to float in their sockets. The grey clothes he was wearing seemed too big for his slight frame.

'We are neighbours, Elizabeth tells me.'

We chat about the cold weather, the economic situation, France's colonial policy.

'We're not through with wars yet, you'll see,' says Eric, reaching for the bottle. 'Another drop?'

I say no thank you and get up.

'I must go, it's getting late.'

Elizabeth kisses me and promises to call me tomorrow. If I closed my eyes, it could be Isabelle talking. I give her a hug.

Back home, everything is quiet. Colette is asleep and the light is off in the sitting room. Robert must have gone to bed early. I imagine him taking a shower, putting on eau-de-cologne, anxious to be forgiven, and I smile.

In the sitting room I notice the flowers arranged in a smaller vase on a low table. I tiptoe into the kitchen, drink a glass of water and eat an apple. I don't want my breath to smell of drink.

I go into the bedroom: the bed is empty. On the bedside table a note: 'Colette is asleep. She asked me to kiss you goodnight for her. I have gone out for a drink. Someone called "Michel" phoned. He will call again tomorrow.'

I re-read the message several times, with my heart beating wildly. The invented commas round 'Michel' make me wonder what to think.

Sunday 9 November

It is ten p.m. Michel has not called.
Perhaps because it's Sunday.

Monday 10 November

I am finding it more and more difficult to sleep. It is as if the more tired I am, the more I fight off sleep. Am I so frightened of the pleasure I might take in being with Louise?

Wednesday 12 November

Michel called. We arranged to have lunch next week. In a restaurant this time. The Petit Saint-Benoît.

Elizabeth has given me the address of her doctor. She thinks he might prescribe me some mild sleeping pills which would at least help me to sleep. I'm not sure about this.

Saturday 15 November

Thinking about it, apart from my dreams, my life is desperately unoriginal. My husband is unfaithful, I am sometimes tempted to be unfaithful too, in spite of that we are very attached and stay together, we both work in offices and we have a little girl who is growing up.

I am ashamed sometimes of my gloomy outlook, and above all of the inner poverty to which I am reduced by my dreams. It is as if they were pumping away all my psychic energy. Where is the enthusiasm and happiness I used to have? I pretend, of course, or rather play-act, since social life calls for it, and I appear to other people to be quite happy. That is not very difficult, since people see only what they want to see.

Can something as commonplace as an abortion really change a women's life for good? What then can one say about the war, the atrocities that everyone around me has been through? Can they have forgotten them? Or are they all play-acting too, acting out some script that calls for forgetfulness?

Sunday 16 November

Last night Robert left for Limoges. He will be there for forty-eight hours. Once again, I didn't fall asleep until it was almost dawn.

This time I dreamed I was introducing Louise to Michel. But I did not dare describe her as my daughter, I introduced her as my niece, the daughter of my sister Isabelle, who died in the camps. Louise began to laugh. 'Mummy is joking, she always teases people, don't listen to her.' I blushed and Michel burst out laughing. The next moment I was in a cell – a prison or a hospital, I don't know which – Colette had been to see me, she was speaking a language I did not understand and when she went, she left behind her latest painting wrapped up in a tartan blanket. I did not dare to look at it, every time my eyes fell on the package, I saw it as a newborn baby all wrapped up, and banged on the door for the nurse to take it away.

I shall never dare speak about Louise to anyone. Robert would be angry, Elizabeth would think I was mad, Michel, too, probably, and he would send me to a psychiatrist.

Michel: it's tomorrow I'm having lunch with him.

Monday 17 November

I don't understand what is happening to me. It is nine in the evening and I, Hannah Périer, have just come from the arms of a man who is not my husband. I feel deliriously happy and haven't the slightest remorse.

I even have the feeling that what is happening to me is a kind of justice.

2 a.m. I can't sleep. Reading what I wrote a few hours ago, I catch myself laughing in the dark: I don't believe in justice, yet I appeal to it at the very moment when I am breaking all the rules of morality. Very edifying.

This was bound to happen from the very first day, it was quite obvious. As soon as we had that drink together, the desire was there, present and shared. We simply gave each other a few social excuses, hiding the truth from ourselves, as a way of pretending that we are not the sort of people to give in to the first temptation.

Not the first, no. But the second time – with honour satisfied – one gives in quickly.

I knew it, as soon as I started telling the joke about the strudel. The pretext came when the dessert arrived. Michel had ordered a pastry with poppy seeds and this Viennese fancy provoked an instant association of ideas.

'Do you know the one about the strudel?'

Michel put down his glass. For a moment I thought I had asked the question for the pure pleasure of watching his face light up with a smile.

'The strudel? Which one?'

'Stop me if you've heard it before. It's about a Jew on his deathbed, an old man. All the family is around him, children and grandchildren. Only Sarah his wife is in the kitchen, making strudel. The smell of it cooking wafts through the house to the dying man's room. He stirs and mutters something. His oldest son David tries to catch his words. "Father, can I do anything for you?" The father frowns, his face contorts, and with a painful effort he stammers out, "David, your mother is making a strudel, it smells delicious and God knows she makes good strudels, the best in the world after my mother's, so before I die, since I know death is in wait for me, I should like to taste it one more time. Go ask your mother for a piece." So David goes out and returns a few minutes later empty-handed. "So?" says the old man. "You asked your mother?" "Yes," says David, "I asked her." "And what did she say?" says the old man. "She said the strudel is for after the funeral."'

Michel greeted the punchline with a burst of laughter, but I, who always laugh at the end of a joke, especially this one, because its black humour usually makes me giggle uncontrollably – this time I found myself overwhelmed by an unexpected sob. Reaching out quickly for my glass to restore my composure, I met Michel's hand. He was already on his feet, close to me, lifting me up, and kissing me. In no time arms, lips. At last.

Tuesday 18 November

I have been to see Elizabeth and confided in her. I had to share my happiness with someone. I don't know if I am really in love, probably not, but I don't care. The happiness is there with all the delicious symptoms that go with it: a light heart, a natural smile on my lips, the urge to walk quickly, to run, even, for no reason, and to talk, to talk to anyone and everyone. Elizabeth listened patiently, then, when I had finished, I realized that she was very depressed.

'What's the matter?'

Eric, her husband, has gone to a drying-out centre for a month. Not for the first time, it seems. Since the end of the war, he has become a complete alcoholic.

'His brother is too.'

'So you're on your own?'

She nods.

'Why not come home with me?'

I put an arm round her shoulders, invite her for supper and she accepts. After all, she hasn't yet met Robert or Colette, it's ridiculous. How could I have let this happen?

'Don't be embarrassed about what I just told you. Robert has been unfaithful to me for a long time now. In spite of all this, we love each other very much. Life is too sad otherwise.'

Elizabeth made no comment. She had to run an errand first and would come round after that.

At home I climb the stairs three at a time as if I had wings. Colette greets me as I come in.

'Somebody telephoned. He'll call back later.'

'He didn't leave his name?'

I know he didn't, and only ask for the brief but intense pleasure of talking about him, of making him exist, here for a second. But Colette has already gone back to her room.

Ten minutes later Elizabeth arrives with a bunch of roses in one hand and a cardboard carton in the other.

'I picked up an apple tart.'

We go into the kitchen, where I start to prepare the meal. Robert ought to be here soon. We talk about Eric. As I wash the lettuce, I curse this wretched war which has broken people's lives. Elizabeth looks down at her hands.

'It wasn't really the war. He was already drinking before that. But I pretended not to know. During the war he drank less, if anything. Alcohol cost more and was harder to find. But since the Liberation, the war has been an excuse. He lets people think that if he drinks, it is because he was deported. Of course, it didn't help. But it's not true.'

'And before the war perhaps he drank because he was going to be deported,' I joke.

At Elizabeth's expression of consternation, I apologize at once. I feel in wickedly good humour and still go on laughing inside at this flippant joke, in very poor taste I admit. As a sort of echo of this internal laughter. I remember what my father always used to say when I did something silly as a child and made him laugh in spite of himself:

'My poor Hannah, you won't try that again.'

Drawn by the sound of our voices, Colette comes into the kitchen, I introduce her to Elizabeth and she kisses her.

'Thank you for the book the other day.'

'Did you like it?' asks Elizabeth.

Absent-mindedly, Colette does not reply, but asks:

'Do you have any children?'

Elizabeth smiles. 'Not yet.'

'Do you want to see my room?' asks Colette.

Elizabeth gets up, Colette takes her by the hand and drags her off. That she should have taken to her so quickly surprises and greatly pleases me. As a rule Colette is rather shy.

Robert comes in just as I finish laying the table. After the introductions, we sit down to eat. Elizabeth goes into raptures over Colette's talent for painting and Colette blushes with pleasure.

'The picture she is painting is really marvellous.'

'Ah, my Christmas present?'

Colette nods.

'Am I allowed to see it, too?' asks Robert.

Colette hesitates but does not withstand her father's smiles for long. She will show him after supper.

We spend a peaceful, domestic sort of evening, as comforting as any I have known for a long time. While I was serving dessert, the phone rang and I took it in the bedroom. It was Michel. Loving, playful, tender. I'm seeing him tomorrow for lunch. I feel young and terribly alive.

Wednesday 19 November

Michel asks me why I have taken it so calmly that Robert is unfaithful to me.

'Are you not jealous?'

I have never put the question in these terms. I explain that a loving relationship is not, to my mind, based on the exclusive possession of the loved one. He shrugs his shoulders, as if he doesn't believe a word of it. He is right, but I cannot tell him what is at the back of my mind without revealing my secret: after all, I have a double life with Louise which I am hiding from Robert; how can I ask Robert for the frankness I cannot offer him myself?

Thursday 20 November

The delight I feel as a result of this affair with Michel spills over into my family life and my feelings for Robert, even the most intimate ones, as if I were suddenly brimful of energy which I need to expend on those I love. Robert greets my outbursts with surprise, while having the tact not to ask any questions. Has he realized that 'someone called "Michel"', as he once wrote, has something to do with it?

Elizabeth came to supper again. Robert likes her and we have agreed to ask her often, especially when she is on her own. Eric will not be back from his cure for another three weeks. Colette likes her too.

It seems to me that if I were not still dreaming of Louise every night, things would be all right. But I sense her hovering over my inner life like a threat.

At the same time, if she were to disappear from my dreams completely, I'm not sure I could bear it.

Tuesday 25 November

Robert came home last night looking as pleased as Punch, with a big bouquet of flowers, and decided to take me out to supper.

'Is this a celebration?' I asked.

'Hush, it's a surprise,' he replied mysteriously.

I gave Colette her supper, Robert read her a bedtime story while I got changed, and we asked Mme Martin, the concierge, to look in about an hour to check that she was asleep.

He took me to the Coupole in Montparnasse. Talkative, relaxed like he was in the old days, he told me about his work, his hopes for promotion. At last, with the dessert, he ordered champagne.

'What is this for? What are we drinking to?'

'To us, to the two of us,' he replied, taking my hand and kissing it. I felt myself blushing and he must have thought it was from emotion, from joy.

'It's over,' he went on. 'I've broken up with Françoise.'

Was I supposed to fall into his arms? I looked down, finding that I had nothing to say. He looked at me for a moment, surprised, disappointed at my lack of reaction, then we talked of other things, of his work again, of Colette's future.

It was not until later, with the light out and holding him in my arms that I realized how happy this made me. How painful it has been, all these years, to share him with someone else.

Then this morning, while Robert was taking a shower, my eyes fell on his wallet on the bedside table. Without really thinking or knowing what I was looking for, I picked it up and went through it. Eventually I found a letter folded in four, opened it and read: 'I realize you are never going to divorce your wife, darling. I am going to marry Henri. In any case, I'm pregnant, and it is not impossible that the child is his. *C'est la vie*. Take care, Goodbye, F.' With shaking hands, I replaced it. Why did I give in to this damned curiosity?

All day the words kept coming back to mind: 'It is not impossible ... ' Was that just a woman's form of revenge?

Wednesday 3 December

This morning I was on the point of telling Robert everything –
about Louise, about Michel, everything. But everything? It took
me all day to realize that he would not understand this
'everything' from which I cannot tear myself away, and, 'telling
all' would mean nothing less than destroying everything we have
between us.

I am marooned with this living lie from which I cannot
escape, the lie that is my version of the truth, the lie, or rather the
silence, which I sometimes fear is going to swallow me up.

Saturday 7 December

As I do every year on St Nicholas' Day, I bought carrots and *speculoos* biscuits for Colette and told her the legend. Not out of religious piety, but out of filial piety, because my mother used to follow the local tradition in Brussels and organize a children's party. For us it was a little foretaste of Christmas and a chance to eat goodies.

This year Colette invited some friends from school, who were delighted with this extra feast day. Elizabeth joined us. She has received a letter from Eric. He is well but will be away two weeks longer than planned. He will be home for Christmas, though.

Friday 12 December

What would I do without Elizabeth? I feel that in her I have found more than a friend, more than a confidant: a sister. We call each other every day and I share with her all my worries and joys, everything.

Well, almost everything. Louise remains my secret.

Wednesday 17 December

My affair with Michel will have lasted exactly a month, to the day. The day before yesterday he asked me to divorce Robert and marry him. I was thunderstruck!

'But I can't even have any children.'

He did not see that as a problem. He says he loves me and can't bear sharing me with someone else. What else can I do but break it off? I am not cut out for deception, and it didn't occur to me that such a misunderstanding between us could ever occur. How could he imagine for a moment that I would leave Robert and Colette?

Preparing for Christmas has distracted me from this parting, but I know I will miss the fun, the pleasure, the shared laughter with him, the energy he gave me to carry on from day to day. So I have decided to organize a party on Christmas Eve. We have invited Eric and Elizabeth. Robert will ask one of his colleagues whom he likes and whose wife has just left him. So we will celebrate Christmas for those without families.

Thursday 18 December

This afternoon Elizabeth took Colette window-shopping. That gave me a chance to do my own shopping: some elegant satin pyjamas for Robert, a new paintbox for Colette, some eau de Cologne for Robert's colleague. For Elizabeth and Eric I can't decide. I want to give them a puppy – my neighbour has one she wants to give away, an adorable black fluffy ball – but I'm afraid they might not be pleased. I'll consult Robert tonight.

On the way back I stopped in front of a beautiful doll. Louise. I'm thinking of her, of course. I can't give her anything, but we would have been giving her a doll like that and she would have laughed, as she does so sweetly, and clapped her hands.

Another Christmas without her. She would be four and a half now.

1948

Sunday 25 January

I woke up with a bad taste in my mouth, my tongue felt heavy as if I had been drugged. A nurse has had to tell me the date, I can't understand where I am, a hospital or nursing-home, it seems. It was she who brought me a pencil and paper. Without seeming interested, she tells me that my husband will be in to see me soon. What has happened? They have brought me some soup, it must be lunchtime. I am a little hungry, and feel exhausted. I will stop writing ...

Just as they were bringing me my food, a doctor came to see me. I don't know his name. He asked me how I felt. I couldn't tell him much, I feel a terrible need to sleep, and can hardly hold this pencil. I am leaving the soup, it has gone cold now anyway ...

It was three o'clock when I woke up again. I can tell the time through the window, from a clock on the building across the road. On the table beside me I find some flowers and a note. I sit up and look: it is from Robert. He came while I was asleep and will be back at the end of the afternoon.

I wonder why I am writing this down. To hang on to life, I suppose, to keep some sort of thread of contact with the world

117

through this familiar, intimate activity. But I feel confused, my memory is all mixed up. Among the threads is a hole I can't explain.

I wanted to get up to go to the bathroom, but when I tried to stand up, the room started to spin. I had to call the nurse. She tells me I have been here nearly a month. How can this be? I have asked to see the doctor again.

Monday 26 January

It is a quarter to nine, they have just taken away my breakfast tray. Yesterday afternoon, just after the doctor's round, Robert arrived and stayed with me until supper – which they serve very early, at six o'clock! – and I went straight off to sleep after that.

At last I have had some explanation of what has happened to me, but the picture is very incomplete. First of all, yes, I have been drugged, which explains why I feel so sleepy. I have been undergoing some kind of sleep-cure. Why? On that point no one has given me a clear explanation and my memory fails me; I try in vain, but just come up against a sort of sickening blank.

The doctor tried to reassure me, and promised to see me again today. He will be back several times a day if necessary, to help me remember. For the moment he is sticking to the following formula: 'You were very depressed.' Depressed? I don't remember being depressed.

Robert was hardly more forthcoming. He simply told me I had had 'some kind of crisis', after which the doctor decided to send me to hospital. Trying to get some bearings, I asked about dates, but he went on being vague, urging me to rest and above all not to worry. Elizabeth has come to stay to help look after

Colette. She is sleeping in the sitting room and has promised to stay until I get home.

Tuesday 27 January

Nine o'clock. I want to get out of here. Why are they keeping me? Yesterday I refused to take the sleeping pills they have been stuffing down me, the ones that keep me in this fog of confusion and stop me remembering. I feel much better now, and I want to get out.

I have just seen the doctor. He says that if all goes well, I can go home in three days. This news cheers me up.

He asked me too whether I was having any dreams. Louise's image immediately came to mind, then, in sequence, the country house, my parents, Isabelle, that procession of true and false memories around which my life has revolved since 1943. I tell him about my parents, that they were deported, about our stay in Belgium, and the more I talk, the more hollow my words come to seem, as hollow as the places I revisited, as hollow as those who were reported to me to be dead, and whose deaths I now realize I cannot believe in, because I did not personally witness them.

When Robert arrived in the late afternoon, I was exhausted and could do no more than tell him that I was coming home, and ask after Colette. My question seemed to bother him, but I can't remember his reply. Unless perhaps I am getting things all mixed up.

I also asked him to bring me a blanket. We are not allowed any extra and the room is badly heated, so every morning I wake up freezing.

Wednesday 28 January

This morning I thought I would go for a walk in the corridor, thinking it would do me good. I did not imagine the sight that met me. At this time of day the doors of all the rooms are open, and the nurses and cleaners come and go among the patients without looking at them, while the patients do not seem to take any notice of anyone either. Some lie back in their wheelchairs, others drift about like sleepwalkers. All I could see were vacant eyes, uninhabited faces, destroyed people. Even the young ones look old. Now and then one sees a doctor, walking past quickly and silently, as if in a hurry to find some human beings to talk to.

So what I feared has happened at the moment I least expected it. When? My memory is coming back in fragments. Now I can see the Christmas tree, Elizabeth, Robert. But where is Colette? Just as I was asking myself this question, I saw Robert pushing open the glass door at the end of the corridor. I was going to meet him when I saw under his arm the tartan blanket from home. My eyes misted over, I had to lean against the wall, my legs began to buckle under me. Luckily Robert was there to help me back to my room.

Did I pass out? I find Robert is beside me, I feel his hand holding mine, yet he seems far away. I'm frightened, terribly frightened. What have I done to my daughter? What have I done to Colette?

'Calm down, take it easy.'

I close my eyes, the better to breathe, but that blanket is still there, Robert put it at the foot of the bed, it was the one the picture was wrapped in. I remember now, my Christmas present ...

When I woke up again at four o'clock, Robert had gone. For the first time in weeks I can recall my dream. Louise was coming down out of a picture to kiss me. She smelt of oil paint, but I quickly realized that she was covered in it, her fingers, legs, clothes, paint was dripping off her everywhere and the colours were fading, she was becoming very pale. I called Colette to help give her her colours back, but Colette wouldn't come, she was cross with me. Just then Elizabeth intervened: 'You must understand her, *after what you did to her.*' I did understand. But when I woke up, I tried in vain to remember. What did I do to her? Why does Robert not talk to me about her? Why was he so ill at ease yesterday? I don't understand. And I'm frightened.

Why have they shut me up in here with all these mad people? ...

The doctor returns. I start to tell him about the memories that are coming back, Christmas, the party, and the memories that won't come, why my daughter is not there, the blanket, the picture. Does he know something? Instead of answering, he asks me if I remember what was in the picture. Instead of reality, my dream comes to mind, Louise, and if I start talking about her I really will want to certify me. It's impossible. But instead of saying nothing, I hear myself saying:

'Yes, I remember a house, a country house, with a cedar tree.'

After the event, the image appears before my eyes, so distinctly that it seems real, and I begin retching violently. I see the picture now: it is the country house of my dream, with the cedar and the terrace, and I see Colette's face, delighted with the surprise she has prepared for me, and even more clearly the look of stupefaction which must have come over my own face. I hear voices all round expressing admiration: 'This little girl is very gifted.' 'Did you copy it from somewhere, or did you make it all up, Colette?' But Colette

124

does not reply, she goes on staring at me. I don't understand that she wants me to be like the others, to admire it and kiss her, in fact I don't understand anything, I lose control and feel suddenly possessed by an unknown and fearful energy which fills me with terror and which I must discharge somehow. I suddenly realize that I have committed some terrible act, an act I cannot bring myself to remember, which has justified my being shut up here. Just as I am looking at the doctor to ask if he knows what I have done, Robert comes in.

'Is this a bad moment?'

'No, not at all, it's just the right moment. I think your wife has some questions to ask you now.'

Before leaving the room, the doctor shakes my hand.

'I'll see you again tomorrow. Above all, don't worry. You are well on the mend.'

I do feel better, I feel warmer.

Robert brings biscuits and a bar of chocolate. He puts them on the window sill, then sits at the foot of the bed and looks at me. This won't do, he is too far away, I ask him to come closer, to come and sit by me, I'll make room for him, I need him to be very close. He comes and sits with his back against the pillows and I put my head on his chest and my arms around him.

'Robert, tell me ... '

But I can't go on, I can't do anything. Something inside has shaken loose, something nameless, as if I had been walled up behind a dam, and I suddenly burst into scalding tears, great tearing sobs which shake me through and through and relieve me. Robert strokes my hair, mutters, 'My love,' and the tears flow even faster, but they are already gentler, how could I have been able to leave my family for so long, what universe has kidnapped me, why am I not at home now, I want to go home. Robert stays until the nightlights go on in the corridor as the lamps go off in the rooms. He doesn't move and for a long time I breathe in the smell of his jacket, soaked with my tears, a smell of tweed, dust and the faint trace of eau-de-cologne.

'Robert, tell me, what did I do?'

He sits up carefully. It is dark and I can hardly make out his face.

'You don't remember at all?'

'No, I don't remember.'

'You broke the picture.'

I broke the picture?

'Was that all?'

Robert hesitates. 'Yes.'

'You're not telling me everything.'

'Yes, I am.'

'No, I heard it in your voice, you hesitated.'

'Well, you tried to hit Colette, too, but I stopped you.'

Colette. My daughter. I'm shattered.

'Is she angry with me?'

'I don't know. She was certainly shocked. Because she couldn't understand. You'll have to explain it to her.'

'What did you tell her?'

'Nothing.'

'What do you mean, nothing? That can't be true.'

'Well, what was I supposed to say?'

He is right. I have no explanation myself. The only possible one, Louise, would make me seem even more sinister to them.

It's night-time, Robert has to go, and kisses me.

'Are *you* angry with me?'

I don't know why I ask him this, I suppose because it is worrying me. But he smiles and kisses me again.

'Of course not, don't be crazy.'

I laugh at this choice of words, which might seem unfortunate, and the idea crosses my mind that if he really did think I was crazy, he would not have said that. He laughs in turn, a bit puzzled, and kisses me once more before making for the door.

As he is about to go out, I call to him:

'Tell me. Colette ... '

Words fail me.

'Yes?'

'Tell me ... she is alive, isn't she?'

I see his eyes widen with shock. He comes back and puts his arms around me.

'Of course she is! What on earth did you think?'

The tears well up again, but I breathe more easily, and let him go. After he has gone, I lie for a few minutes in the dark, and let

126

this nocturnal calm I need so much wash over me, before putting the light on to write this down. It is very late now, my eyes are closing, everyone is asleep, I am worn out.

Saturday 31 January

I am home at last. I came back yesterday, Robert brought me in the car. Elizabeth and Colette were waiting at the door. When I arrived, they came forward, Elizabeth with her hand on Colette's shoulder, I leaned forward to kiss them, first Colette, then Elizabeth, it was a little cool and ceremonious, as when one meets up with people one has not seen for a long time and doesn't quite know how to approach, then Elizabeth suggested a cup of tea and I went into the sitting room.

There have been some changes in my absence. In the sitting room the sofa has been moved and set at right angles to a double bed covered with cushions. I asked Robert why things had been changed and he explained in an embarrassed way that it was because Elizabeth had been sleeping there while I was away, she had organized the new arrangement. I didn't want to argue. I suppose she means well, and anyway the flat is spotless and well cared for. I thanked her warmly for that.

While we were drinking our tea, I thought Colette was watching me with unusual and particularly close attention. Elizabeth was busying herself, anxious to anticipate my least wish, so that I felt almost like a visitor.

We couldn't talk much, of course. I was tired and also quite moved to be home. We just exchanged small talk about the discomforts of hospital life, the terrible food they give you, then Robert suggested I should rest.

Changes have been made in the bedroom, too. The double bed Elizabeth has been sleeping in is actually ours. Robert has replaced it with twin beds. They are quite nice, but I don't understand why he did not simply buy a single divan and put it in the sitting-room, that would have been the obvious solution. I take care not to say anything, though, the more so since Elizabeth, who made the cushions, bought the material and so on, was present and waiting for my verdict. When I thanked her for going to all this trouble, she simply said:

'You said you suffer from insomnia, so I thought ... Well, this way you won't disturb each other.'

I agreed, assuring her that it was fine. There will be plenty of time to sort out this kind of detail later.

Sunday 1 February

When I came out of hospital, the doctor told me to take a month's sick leave – he thinks I should still be keeping very quiet – and prescribed sleeping pills to prevent the return of my insomnia. Thanks to him, I know now that there are several kinds of insomnia, the kind where you are in a drowsy state (which I was suffering from before my spell in hospital), and the kind where you wake up after a few hours and cannot get back to sleep until dawn. He advised me to rest, then when I feel strong enough, to walk out for at least two hours a day, and to find some kind of distraction. What more attractive prescription could there be? If he did not mention some therapeutic love-making, I suppose it was only out of respect for propriety.

Love-making is not favoured by the new arrangement of our bedroom. I slept in my new bed for the first time, or rather I tried to, for I couldn't sleep a wink in this narrow bed, it felt like being back in hospital, and knowing that Robert was six feet away but out of bounds, far away in sleep, made my loneliness even more unbearable. Before, at least when I couldn't sleep, I could move up against him, feel the warmth of his body, I would keep as still as possible and I don't think I ever woke him. What is all this nonsense about twin beds? It is something I had better raise with

Robert, Elizabeth is not to blame, she was just doing her best, and our private life is not her business anyway.

She stayed the night again, in the sitting-room, as is her habit now, and she wanted to take Colette to school this morning. I think she could go home now. I should be glad if she can do some shopping for me now and again, since she lives nearby it should not be too difficult for her to go a little out of her way, but from now on I would like her help to be confined to that.

I need to feel at home in my own house, with my family. Of course I can't say this straight out, it would be tactless, but surely with her delicacy of feeling she will realize this without my having to insist.

When I came home, I found in the pile of mail awaiting me a little note from Michel, scribbled on his surgery stationery. It is hard to read, as if all self-respecting doctors have to make their writing completely illegible. 'My dear Hannah,' I finally made out, 'I have heard that you were unwell. I would be glad to have news of you and see you again. Give me a call. Affectionately, Michel.' Who told him I was unwell? I am too tired to call him. I'll be sure to do it tomorrow or the day after. If only to find out the answer.

Louise has grown taller again. I am struck by the fact that she does not look like anyone else in the family. She has long hair now, dark and curly, and some nights my dream is devoted to trying out different hairstyles on her, from plaits to bunches, or a pony tail, and every time she laughs at the new look, runs away and undoes it, preferring to keep her hair loose down her back. She is no coquette, more of a tomboy, if anything. Other times I bath her and wash her hair, and she plays with the shampoo, concocting temporary hairstyles by making her hair stick up in all directions. She has a thin, muscular body, with white skin and long, thin hands and feet.

I dreamed last night that I was going to bed, here in our bedroom, and that she was sleeping in the other bed instead of Robert. In fact she wasn't sleeping. I was going to bed late and she was waiting, wanting me to read a story, bringing a book out from under the covers, the tales of Hans Andersen.

'Mummy, read me *The Snow Queen.*'

I knew she had chosen it because it was the longest. I sat down beside her and began to read. But I had hardly started when she interrupted me:

'Sing me a song. You know, "Soldier, soldier".'

> Oh, soldier, soldier, won't you marry me
> With your musket, fife and drum?
> Oh, no, sweet maid, I cannot marry thee
> For I have no boots to put on!

Louise laughed and laughed.
'Go on!'
I went on:

> So up she went
> To her grandfather's chest
> And brought him some boots
> Of the very, very best
> And the soldier put them on ...

Then she interrupted me:
'Mummy, you're not going to die, are you?'
She knew that I had been ill and in hospital.
'No, of course not. Whatever gives you that idea?'
Louise looked at me reproachfully and I blushed and corrected myself:
'Well, yes, of course I will die one day, but not yet. Not yet.'
'When, then?'
'When you are grown up enough.'
'Then I'm going to stay teeny tiny, always.'
She hid her head under the sheets, I tried to catch her, but I couldn't find her, I searched in vain: she had vanished.

When I woke up, my reply was still ringing in my ears: 'When you are grown up enough.' Are we ever grown up enough to lose someone we love?

I am very bothered. Elizabeth came back at lunchtime, and I had a long argument with her, but she would not give in. I explained to her that I felt better now, that she could go home to Eric, but she replied that Eric was away on another cure, that he would be away for a few weeks and that she was very happy to stay and look after Colette. She went on to say that I was still too tired to be running the household on my own, she had agreed this with Robert. I will have to talk to him tonight.

Another new arrangement is that Colette stays for the
hour after school and waits for Elizabeth to pick her up b
coming home. The result is that I find it impossible to be o
own with my daughter for a single second. Just now, for inst
– it was a little after six when they came home. Colette can
kiss me, then retreated to her room. When I went after he
have a little talk, Elizabeth appeared immediately on the pre
of asking me if I wanted something to drink. I thanked her,
the result was that Colette followed her into the kitchen. As it
were avoiding me. It is almost as if they are in league. And w
Colette has been watching me carefully since I came back,
avoids meeting my eyes.

This morning I called Michel. He will come round tomorrow at midday to take me for a walk in the Luxembourg Gardens. He sounded kindly, almost brotherly. Why should he not become a real friend, now that we know our limits? He is a straightforward and honest person, full of good qualities.

Last night, when everyone had gone to bed, I had a conversation with Robert. Since Elizabeth was on the other side of the door, in the sitting room, we had to whisper. I find even this intrusion on our privacy unbearable. If we were to make love – not that we have, since I got back – she would hear everything. That was what I told him, and also my feeling that Elizabeth is running our lives, especially that she is coming between Colette and me. Robert spoke up for her, pointed out how kind she has been when I was away, said that without her he would not have been able to manage – but he did so only half-heartedly. He also admitted that she should not take up so much room in our lives and that it 'would probably be preferable', his words, if she went back home. But he does not want to be the one to tell her. He thinks that coming from him, the request would seem rude and ungrateful. He said that she is my friend, after all, and it is easier for women to settle this kind of delicate matter between

Wednesday 4 February

Michel will be here in an hour, but I don't have the strength to go out with him. I did not sleep a wink all night, and feel literally worn out.

Last night, on the other hand, when Elizabeth and Colette came home, I was feeling fine. I had spent the afternoon relaxing and listening to music and I felt full of determination to tackle Elizabeth. To show her that I was better, I had started preparing dinner. The table was laid, the salad washed, a pot of tea was ready. But instead of being pleased with this progress, she seemed to take offence.

'You are being unwise, you'll make yourself ill again.'

I have long lost the habit of being mothered like this, and normally I would have put her in her place. But not wishing to start the evening on the wrong foot, I simply shrugged my shoulders casually and reassured her:

'No. Really, it's fine, I feel much better today.'

Colette was observing us carefully, as if she was watching us score points.

Then Elizabeth noticed that I had only laid three places and turned to me:

'Are you not eating with us?' she asked.

I realized at the time that this was an odd, inappropriate question. Why, seeing three places, was it the least likely possibility (since I had just said I felt better and since I had laid the table) that came first to her mind? But without lingering over this, I put on a naïve and innocent expression and explained that Robert had telephoned to say he was staying late at work. This news visibly annoyed her; instead of coming to drink the tea I had ready, she went straight into the kitchen – where there was very little left to do – and busied herself there until it was time to sit down at the table. Colette had shut herself up in her room meantime, and I didn't try to see her, thinking I would tackle each problem in its own time.

The atmosphere at supper remained tense, with each of us playing a role, while I had the peculiar feeling that we were not in the same play. Elizabeth asked Colette about her day at school, as a mother might, while maintaining a cool distance from me, and Colette replied in monosyllables, giving me uncertain looks from under her lashes. As for me, I was pretending not be there, if I can put it that way.

At last Colette's bedtime arrived. After cleaning her teeth, she came to kiss me goodnight. I wanted to hug her and say something, but Elizabeth was waiting in the doorway, looking at me, so I preferred to let her go.

Waiting for Elizabeth to return, I realize now that I was trembling with fright. I was prepared for this, but I suddenly had a presentiment that Elizabeth would resist. Since I have been home, something about her – something I have not been able to put my finger on but which seems almost a tangible presence between us – has changed. She has been perfectly pleasant, patient, attentive, but her attitude has had something cold and distant about it, something impersonal. She is no longer the bosom friend, the sister I thought I had found in her, but a sort of model nurse, fully professional, with whom I feel no complicity or friendship. Is it my stay in hospital which has somehow changed my own attitude?

I decided at first not to take any notice of this negative impression. To sort out the present situation amicably, I urgently needed to be back on a footing of confidence with her. So when she rejoined me in the sitting-room, I invited her to come and sit by me and have a drink.

'Don't you think you ought to go to bed?' she said quietly, in a last attempt to avoid the confrontation she could see coming.

I smiled as sweetly as possible as I replied:

'It's very early and I wouldn't be able to get to sleep. Besides, I'd like us to have a talk.'

'A talk?'

She stiffened and I went on calmly, but with more determination than I had the day before: I really ought to be taking charge of my life now; the help she had given had been immensely precious to us but now it was imperative for my own and my family's sake that we get back to our normal pattern of living.

'I don't see how my presence prevents that,' she replied, tilting her head provocatively, in a way unusual for someone who is as a rule so discreet.

Adopting a strategy that Michel taught me, I looked her straight in the eyes.

'Really? You don't see?'

She blushed deeply and to hide her embarrassment – which was greater than I expected – she got up and walked around the room.

'No, I don't see,' she went on after a moment. 'I think, on the contrary, that my being here has allowed your family to keep going, which it might not have done otherwise.'

Thinking that she had said either too much or too little, I invited her, with some anxiety, I confess, to say what she meant. She came and sat down beside me again. She was calm now and I saw an expression of deep pity come over her face.

'My poor Hannah, do you even remember what happened?'

Since my return, I had not spoken about this with her. This recent past, so painful that I still had not really recalled it, was something I had spoken about only with Robert. Had I forgotten that Elizabeth was there, too? Now that she asked me, the truth hit me.

She must know; so does Colette. And Robert.

They all know.

Everyone knows except me.

Trembling, and on the defensive, I simply replied, with an involuntary note of bravado in my voice:

'I destroyed the picture Colette had painted for me.'

Elizabeth let a few minutes go by. Why was she not saying anything, unless to make me feel I had not told the whole story? At last, looking me in the eyes, she asked:

'Do you know *how* you destroyed it?'

How? What did she mean? No, of course I did not remember. Robert had only told me that it had happened; it had stirred a faint memory for me, but nothing precise.

My silence spoke for me. Elizabeth gave a deep sigh and gave me the following story, more or less in these words:

'My dear Hannah, I would have preferred not to tell you. Robert and I had agreed not to upset you with this story, but since you are insisting that I go home, you have to know. On Christmas Eve, when Colette gave you the picture she had been painting for you for months, with such love, you did something, well, extremely upsetting and very traumatic for us all, and especially for your daughter. You picked up the knife that had been used to carve the venison and you—' she hesitated a moment – 'yes, you slashed the canvas in an almost murderous frenzy. Then ...'

I interrupted her.

'Then?'

Worried by my question, she looked at me. I felt stabbing pains behind my eyes, at my temples, in my neck.

'Then?' I repeated, more loudly.

She looked at me again, passed her hand across her forehead as if to wipe away the last traces of remorse and went on in a shaking voice:

'Then, still holding the knife – things happened so quickly and we were so stunned that nobody reacted to stop you – you turned on Colette and raised your arm ... '

I could listen to no more. With an energy I did not think I had in me, I stood up and shouted:

'It's not true, it's a lie! None of that is true!' and rushed into my bedroom, where I collapsed on my bed, my heart pounding and my eyes dry.

I confess that at that moment I truly wanted to kill Elizabeth. And the desire to kill was not just in my heart and guts, but in my arms, my hands, my fingertips. It felt almost as if I was committing the act.

To try to calm down, I shut my eyes and began to take long slow breaths, trying not to think about anything. I did not have to try very hard. The shock I had received had drained my spirit.

Once I was calmer, after about half an hour, I went back into the sitting room. I say 'calmer'; that is one way to put it, but I actually felt more serene and self-assured than I have ever been, cold and unreachable, as if possessed of some icy rage, pitilessly rational. I had to understand, to understand and know everything. Everything. Even the worst.

I made Elizabeth take up the story where she had left off; my aim was for her to stick as closely as possible to what she had seen. I had raised my arm, she said, and was it at that point that Robert had intervened? She confirmed it. Yes, Robert had stopped me, but Colette had fled to her room in tears, and – according to Elizabeth – 'traumatized for life'.

'Do you understand? She's frightened of you now, and I had to promise to protect her.'

As I remained silent, Elizabeth went on:

'She's the one who wants me to stay, but she will never dare admit this if you ask her. She is too afraid of you now.'

So that was it: the truth. Was it really the truth? I couldn't believe it. Yet everything fitted – Robert's unease, Elizabeth's presence, Colette's behaviour. In a robot-like trance, I thanked Elizabeth for being so frank, and went back to my room. I was stunned, unable to think.

That was how Robert found me when he came home, lying on the bed staring at the ceiling, and I was still in the same state this morning, even more exhausted, but just as disoriented and unable to answer his questions. I let him go off looking worried, without having been able to report to him a word of my conversation with Elizabeth. What could I tell him that he doesn't already know?

Michel is about to arrive. Even the prospect of talking to someone seems impossible.

Thursday 5 February

It is still Louise who brings me the most joy in the end. When I manage to sleep – which has become as difficult as it was before my stay in hospital, I wonder whether I ought to keep on taking the sleeping pills, which make me feel drowsy without helping me sleep – when I am back in her cheerful, carefree company, with her bright eyes and clear laughter, I feel as if a door opens up inside me, a door leading to a zone of liberty which I may have lost for good in real life. At the same time, it is never an unmixed pleasure, I wake up feeling guilty about this illusory happiness, neither shared nor shareable, a happiness that takes me away from those close to me, digging between them and me a trench that grows bigger every day.

In the end I did go out with Michel yesterday. When he arrived, I was feeling exhausted, but in his patient and kindly way he managed to persuade me that the fresh air would do me good, it was a fine day, so I wrapped up warmly and followed him. In the Luxembourg Gardens the air had that clarity that cold dry weather sometimes – so rarely – brings to Paris. The dark bare branches of the trees stood out against the blue sky with unreal distinctness. We walked slowly up and down, like an elderly couple taking care not to overdo it for their health's sake. Michel took my arm and I said nothing. We stopped for a few minutes by the silent wooden horses on springs and for a moment I thought about Colette, who used to be so good at pretending to gallop, urging on her steed, and I thought, my God, of Louise too. Did I lean rather heavily on Michel's arm? He must have sensed I was tired, since he suggested we go back and have a drink near Saint-Sulpice.

'How did you hear I was ill?'

In the steamed-up atmosphere of the café Michel was sitting facing me, as if to express both distance and closeness – distance of the body but closeness of the eyes, and steady support. While he was speaking he did not take his eyes off me.

'It was Elizabeth who told me. In a rather odd way, I thought.'

He told me how she had booked an appointment at his surgery, on the pretext of a gynaecological problem, and then how the conversation had gone.

'You must understand, I had never met her. She hadn't told me she was coming on your behalf.'

It was only at the end of the conversation that she had spoken about me, without giving any details.

'She said only that you had been taken to hospital and would surely be glad to have the support of your friends. She even added something about Robert – I can't remember quite what she said. But it was along the lines that he was not always as supportive of you as he might be. I thought this was an indiscretion and found it rather shocking.'

I was dumbstruck. Why had Elizabeth gone to such lengths? How could she have thought that my taking her into my confidence authorized her to take a step like this? I can't fathom the feeling of unease which has gripped me since I came home – the impression that a net is being drawn about me, every day restricting my movements a little more, forcing me into a certain path, determining my life.

As I said nothing, Michel asked:

'Does she know about us?'

She did indeed. I told Michel how in the exhilaration of the first few days after we met, I had confided in Elizabeth. He nodded.

'And now?'

Now? The question was unexpected and I heard myself replying:

'Now she decides everything. I think she has decided she wants to push me over the edge into madness.'

After letting fall these first words, which came out as a confession, to my own surprise, the rest of the story spilled out freely: being taken to hospital, my amnesia, the broken picture, the fragmentary memories that had come back, my return home, Elizabeth's insistence on staying to care for Colette. And, finally, the version of events she had given me. The knife. Colette. Michel listened attentively, his face expressing pity and astonishment by turns, when I stopped speaking, it was starting to get dark, he took my hands in his and enclosed them in his warmth.

'And now,' he said again, 'what are you going to do?'

A moment earlier, I would not have known what to say. What door in my head is he knocking on, since his questions all provoke an answer?

'I'm going to look for the picture. I must find it, it must still be in the house.'

Michel nodded his approval, and stood up.

'I'll take you back now.'

We walked back, arm in arm like an old couple. At the door to our building, he kissed me briefly on the forehead.

'Let me know how things are, won't you? I'm counting on you.'

He hesitated, then added:

'I would watch out with Elizabeth. For the moment, if I were you, I wouldn't confide in her.'

I smiled. For some time now, I have lost all confidence in her, but it's reassuring that he thinks the same and says so: if I can trust my own intuition, if it bears any relation to reality, it must mean that I have not yet lost my sanity.

Friday 6 February

I have had a nightmare, which told me what I already know: I am afraid of Elizabeth with a deep irrational fear, no doubt drawing on earlier fears dating back to the war, the fear of being found out, denounced, being singled out for what I am, something I can't help and also, it must be said, something I hold on to. Can one deny one's own truth and stay sane? And when one sees other people so devoured by self-hate that they turn it on the rest of the world, how can one avoid proclaiming one's own identity like a banner? People do not kill because they hate other people, they kill to avoid killing themselves, because they hate themselves. Murder, in mankind, in every nation, is the last defence against suicide. But the more they kill, the less they can bear themselves, and that is how wars carry on and never stop.

I don't believe there has ever existed an ideal regime, that would work for everyone. But I believe that if the politicians who rule us really wanted peace between the nations, they would find a way to have it respected. If they have not done so, it only proves what we knew already: self-hate is stronger than love of our fellow-men. If he sees his neighbour become a victim of crime, the man in the street, who is never short of arguments to justify cowardice, looks first to protect himself.

Munich certainly proved that.

Munich: cowardice and wretchedness. But was I any less of a coward? So as to escape, and protect myself, I changed my name, agreed to deny my identity, to sever my links with my family. Is it this betrayal that Louise is reminding me of every night? Is it into this fatal crack, caused by being untrue to myself and the history of my people, that the shadow of madness has crept in? I dreamed last night that Elizabeth had decided to redecorate the whole flat, and was turning out all the cupboards, knocking down walls, prying into every corner. In a disused cupboard in my bedroom she found Louise, Louise crouching in the dark, with staring eyes, red from crying, Louise begging for mercy. Delighted with her discovery, Elizabeth told her to come out, but Louise wouldn't. I implored Elizabeth to leave her alone, I beg you, leave her, she is doing no harm to anyone.

'Oh, so you know who she is?'

Elizabeth's question had a triumphant ring to it, like the examining magistrate who has finally found the decisive piece of evidence and senses that the accused is about to confess. Like a condemned woman, I hung my head and signed my death warrant:

'Yes, she is my daughter.'

Elizabeth's sarcastic laughter woke me up, and it took me a few seconds to realize that she was indeed laughing in the next room. I waited a bit before getting up, remembering my confession – 'she is my daughter' – and the unexpected and all too short relief it had brought me.

I spent the morning searching Colette's bedroom. At first I thought that she had thrown out all her pictures and her paints. I found nothing at all, and the tidiness that seemed to have taken over seemed odd and unnatural, at last I found behind her wardrobe what I was looking for: all her canvases, face to the wall, and in a corner the new paintbox I had given her. Out of curiosity, I opened it, everything was still brand-new, Colette had not touched it. My heart beating quickly, I took the paintings out of their hiding place, and looked at them. They almost all brought back some happy occasion, I had not realized my memory held so many. I was overcome with emotion at this secret reunion with my daughter's past, a past we have shared and in which, although I often failed to pay enough attention, we had been closely united, a past that is not at all distant, but from which we have been so suddenly cut off. I am also moved by the talent in the pictures and devastated that it has been thwarted, and all through my fault. Will she ever be able to forgive me?

I kept looking, but in vain, the Christmas picture did not seem to be there, all that was left was a canvas-stretcher, broken in the middle, as if … as if what? Suddenly, the scene comes back to me. As if memory lies in a remembered gesture, I suddenly feel the release through my leg and the impact of wood and canvas on the tip of my shoe, I was wearing high-heeled court shoes and black stockings that night, I had taken the picture in both hands and my foot had gone through the canvas before I realized it.

I know, too, that I was aiming at a particular place: in the middle of the picture, on the terrace, Colette had painted two children skipping, two little girls. Why two? Before I had kicked it, I asked her, or at least it seems to me that I asked her, unless I dreamed it later in hospital, I can hear my voice saying, 'Why two little girls?' and Colette replying, 'Mummy, why don't you give me a little sister?'

At last, rolled up in the back of the wardrobe, underneath her shoes, I found the canvas. There are no knife marks on it, but there is a hole in the middle, a hole that could be repaired, in fact, since nothing is missing, one would just have to bring the edges together and fit them properly.

Before leaving the room, I put everything back as it was, except for the canvas, which I have taken into my room and hidden under my mattress. It is almost midday and Elizabeth will soon be back.

Saturday 7 February

Light has finally been shed on all this. Not the best of lights, true, but at least it is light. And I have begun to breathe again.

First of all, Robert. Last night, I surprised a conversation between him and Elizabeth. We had been in our beds for some time when he leaned over to mine and called my name softly. Why did I not reply? I was dozing but not quite asleep, still thinking about the canvas, now lying under my mattress – why had Elizabeth invented the story of the knife, if not to assert her power over me by terrifying me? But I still did not know one thing: what was Robert's part in all this? Was he an accomplice in Elizabeth's lie? It seemed impossible. But it was also impossible that he was not somehow mixed up in this sinister strategy. What had happened between them in my absence? As I did not reply, Robert must have thought I was asleep and tiptoed out into the sitting-room. Hardly had he closed the door than I jumped up and went to listen at the door. At first I could not make out the words, rapid whispers in which there seemed to be more irritation than complicity or tenderness. Then the voices became louder. They were muttering now, and snatches of words reached me. Robert wanted something, in his voice there was a begging tone which tore at my heart, but Elizabeth was protesting, obstinately refusing whatever it was. I suppose any other woman in my place would have thought the worst. It naturally crossed my mind, but I did not believe it for a second. I know Robert too well, his sense of morality, to believe that he would try to seduce a woman under my roof, in my presence. But what else could he possibly be asking her for, that she had a right to refuse? I found out soon enough.

The voices ceased and I just had time to jump back into bed before Robert opened the door and came back to bed. He looked at me, realized that my eyes were open and came over.

'You're awake.'

I smiled in the dark and simply moved over to make room for him. He slipped in beside me.

'Were you awake just now?'

I hugged him.

'Why do you let her torment you?'

He didn't reply.

'You have slept with her, haven't you?'

As he still said nothing, I went on, letting my imagination reconstruct the story.

'It must have been when I was in hospital. One night when you were depressed, she took advantage, there was a vacancy after all, the lady of the house out of the way, possibly for ever. And she decided to take my place. Is that it?'

He said nothing but I could feel that he was convulsed with emotion, he held me tight, trembling all over, burying his head in my neck, Robert, no, I beg you, please don't cry.

Later on we found each other again in the night, for a long time, tenderly, and went to sleep together. In the morning, I could not remember having any dreams.

We have decided to wait a little before settling the Elizabeth problem. Not that there is any doubt about it: she must go and as soon as possible – but we have to work out a strategy. Colette is too directly involved for us to rush things, and she needs some explanation. Above all, I must make direct contact with her and win back her confidence.

Sunday 8 February

We cannot send Elizabeth away without speaking to Colette. At first Robert wanted to do just that. 'She can just pack her bags and go.' But I was against it. Even though I would like this too, confronting Colette with a *fait accompli* seems dangerous. What if Elizabeth were to convince her that she is the victim of a plot? I don't know what Colette has been thinking, perhaps she will never really understand all this and will distrust me, distrust us, until the end of her days.

Besides, now that I know that Robert is back at my side, I feel full of strength and well able to stand up to Elizabeth for however long it takes to outface her. I have lost the impatience of the powerless, the foolish haste that sends those who panic flying into the abyss they are trying to escape. Yesterday, without my realizing it, a cold war was declared, a war without mercy, and a war I do not have the right to lose. I owe it to my daughter to win.

Monday 9 February

'Vengeance is a dish better eaten cold.' Now I know what that means. When I first encountered this saying as a child – my mother must have used it, about something long forgotten – the idea seemed ridiculous. Someone who seeks revenge is surely not cold, but burning with the flames of vengeance. What I did not know is precisely how cold that passion can be. Perhaps this is real hatred. When there is some flame left, it means there is still some love.

From now on, I am treating Elizabeth with distant politeness, as if she were a stranger. I take advantage of being at home all the time to make her feel that, whatever she says, she is my guest, a guest who has outstayed her welcome but whom I am nevertheless treating with all the courtesy required by the laws of hospitality, I have taken over the reins of the household and this change makes me deeply happy. On her side, she is seeking to carry it off with dignity, but her graciousness deceives nobody. I know she is uneasy and seething with repressed anger, I would admire her tenacity if I did not find it monstrous.

The hardest thing to bear is the way she manipulates Colette between us as if she were a hostage. She is constantly spoiling her now, allowing her to do anything she likes, and she tries to discredit any of my attempts to intervene. This morning for instance, at breakfast, Colette smothered her bread with jam, and I could not resist pointing this out:

'That's far too much jam, it's bad for you.'

Elizabeth hastened to interrupt:

'Bad for her? Nonsense. That jam is made with pure fruit and sugar, I bought it myself. It's very good for her!'

Colette, with an air of victory, looked at me as she dipped her spoon into the jam pot again.

'Stop it, Colette! If you eat all that sugar ...'

But Colette had already put the spoon in her mouth. Elizabeth was encouraging her with a smile, I will have to alter my tactics. I smile too, and change the subject. Since Elizabeth sees to it that Colette and I are never alone together, I decide to say something in her presence, as if she were not there.

'Colette. I'm so sorry about the picture. I am afraid I must have upset you a lot.'

Surprised, Colette puts down her spoon and looks anxiously at Elizabeth. She in turn looks transfixed. Did she think that her melodramatic fantasy would put the subject out of bounds for ever? Pleased with the effect I have produced, I go on:

'Daddy and I have talked it over a lot. It is true that I did something I never should have done, but one day I will tell you why.'

As I expected, Elizabeth jumped up, beside herself with exasperation.

'You can't possibly explain why! You're sick! In fact, you're mad.'

I laugh and look at Colette, who doesn't know what to do and hesitates. Elizabeth's outburst has shocked her, which was exactly what I wanted.

'Mad? Me?'

I laugh again and, still talking to Colette as if Elizabeth were not there:

'You know, I saw the doctors in the hospital, Colette. When people are mad, they don't let them go home. If you like, I'll take you to see the doctor who was looking after me, and he can tell you. Would you like that?'

Colette cannot take her eyes off me. She does not yet dare agree with me, but she is close to it, she is looking at me genuinely now, no longer as if she is judging some stranger, it is my daughter's true expression. Elizabeth at that moment takes her by the hand and tries to pull her away.

'You are going to be late for school, come on.'

But Colette escapes from her and rushes at me, before I can stop her she is huddled up on my lap, Colette, my little Coco, my chick, my baby. Hugging me tightly, she does not move, and I put my arms round her, gently, trying to control the affection which for so many days I have been forced to hold back, and which has been stifling me, she says nothing and I do not speak. When Elizabeth brings her coat, she refuses to leave my lap.

'Would you like me to take you to school?'

Colette nods, without daring to look at Elizabeth, who is now very pale.

'But you'll be late, I'm not dressed yet ...'

I hesitate for an instant: should I let Elizabeth take her one more time? It would be a grand gesture, but I am too frightened. Elizabeth will not forgive my victory, and I believe her capable of anything.

'Well, never mind, you'll just have to be late this once, I'll explain to your teacher.'

Without my saying more, Colette runs into my bedroom to wait for me. I turn to Elizabeth.

'Many thanks for your help. I'll manage. Don't be late for work yourself now.'

After taking Colette to school – all the way she clutched my hand without a word, and when I left her I promised to come and fetch her home as I used to, before the study hour – I went to the hospital for a routine check-up. I saw the same doctor, and told him, without going into details, the reasons why I now felt better. They seemed to satisfy him. He thinks I had a fit of depression, aggravated by a particularly vulnerable situation in my emotional life, but he does not think my condition is serious and does not anticipate any future consequences. He advised me to go on taking sleeping pills, since in his view insomnia might lead to fatigue, which predisposes one to further attacks. In short, he gave me some medical waffle embellished with a few skilfully chosen terms, which boils down to: I don't know quite what was wrong with you, and neither do you; don't worry, you will have to live with it. Anyway, you seem to be on the mend.

Before I left, I asked if he would see me again with my daughter. He readily agreed: he has a surgery every day, we can just turn up and he will see us.

This morning I awoke after a very short but incredibly vivid dream. I was in a cobbled courtyard surrounded by high walls, playing ball with Elizabeth. Perhaps I was a child, but it was not very clear. We were taking it in turns to throw a ball against the wall and we were not allowed to catch it until it had bounced at least three times. When Elizabeth did it, she managed it easily. But every time it was my turn, the cobblestones changed shape, got bigger, the cracks between them were wider, and the ball bounced all over the place so that I couldn't catch it. But I seem to know that if I lose this game, Elizabeth will send me to a concentration camp.

It is her turn, she tries hard and suddenly, as she is finishing, I see that my fingertips are bleeding, blood is streaming from them, the flesh is showing, and I know that if I do not press each finger against the corresponding finger on the other hand, I shall bleed to death. Elizabeth has finished, it's my turn, I have a choice between two kinds of death, if I refuse to play I will be deported, if I play and take my hands apart, breaking the circulation of the blood I have restored ... Just at this moment Louise arrives, picks up the ball and takes my place. By some miracle, Elizabeth does not notice the change, watches her as if she were me, and I creep

154

backwards into the shadows, lean against the wall and crouch down to get my breath.

Yesterday, before going to fetch Colette from school, I went for a drink with Michel. When I had told him everything, he said, 'Bravo,' and went on:

'I have been thinking since the other day. Elizabeth's plan was very simple.'

According to him, she had expected that he and I would get together again, which would have enabled her to steal Robert away without such a bad conscience.

'I wonder whether she did not tell him about us?'

Until then that possibility had not occurred to me, but it does not seem so unlikely. One day – later – I will ask Robert. That would be a weight off my mind.

Wednesday 11 February

I took Colette to the hospital. The doctor reassured her and advised her – in a fatherly way – not to trust anyone but me.

'This is your mother. You need her and she needs you. And don't forget that your papa needs you both.'

He played his part to perfection and Colette kissed me when we came out. I took advantage of it to say to her:

'Now we can tell Elizabeth that she can go home.'

Colette did not react. I find it hard to resist the temptation to ask her what Elizabeth has been saying to her about me. But I hold back. This kind of confidence can wait till later. All in good time.

It's over, she's gone. At last.

We did things in a civilized way. Last night I prepared a nice supper and when we reached the dessert, Robert announced that we would drink to the health of our family, now that we were all reunited, and to Elizabeth, who would be able to go home tonight. Colette, who already knew, was not surprised. The only one who was surprised was Elizabeth, who found nothing to say. After supper, Colette said goodbye to her with a brief kiss and went straight to her room. I invited Elizabeth to pack her things, which she did without lingering. Half an hour later, Robert was seeing her home.

While he was away, I changed the sheets on the double bed and we slept there.

Was all that part of her campaign? Did the idea of our sleeping together distress her, was that it?

But I do not want to upset Robert any more. After all, I am not beyond reproach myself.

'Tomorrow, I warn you, I am moving the furniture. We will have the big bed again and the twin beds can be divans.'

Friday 13 February

Last night, as usual, I took a long time to get to sleep, but Robert was in my arms and the night seemed short. I felt I was coming out of a nightmare and that we had won through in some kind of war.

In the early morning, I dreamt of Louise. Of her laughing. Her laughter as I woke up changed into the laughing voice of Colette, who came into our bed in her pyjamas. Life as I love it is beginning again. At last.

1954

Thursday 15 July

A month ago we moved out to this pretty little village near Versailles: Les Loges-en-Josas. When I was sorting things out for the move, I found this diary tucked away in the back of my wardrobe, and felt like starting it again. It was just a passing thought, and I would probably not have followed it up if a coincidence had not thrown a bridge across all the years since I last wrote in it: a few days ago, I saw Elizabeth again.

It must have been on Tuesday. I was in a department store in Paris, queuing at the till, when I heard a voice that sounded familiar, saying, 'Do you take cheques?'

I looked to see who had spoken, but saw at the counter a woman whom I did not recognize from behind. She was wearing high heels, fishnet stockings, a figure-hugging green suit, and at her side was a lively-looking little girl with fair hair, whom I did not know. I was just thinking I had made a mistake when she turned round: and, yes, it was Elizabeth. Completely transformed. Where once she had seemed to be the essence of quiet good taste, she now had permed and dyed auburn hair, and her clothes seemed slightly vulgar. I was just stepping back into my place in the queue when she looked round as if trying to find someone, and spotted me.

'Hannah!' she cried, rushing up. 'How good to see you again!'

Before I could react, she had kissed me on both cheeks.

'Lulu, come here,' she called to the little girl, who was hanging back. 'This is Hannah, an old friend of mine. Hannah, let me introduce my daughter, Marie – we call her Lulu for short.'

I smiled to hide my emotions.

'That's an unusual way to shorten Marie!' I said.

But Elizabeth was not listening, she was looking around again.

'I'm waiting for my husband. I don't know where he can have got to.'

'Eric?'

'Oh, no, we're divorced. You knew of course that Eric didn't want children. I married Bruno about five years ago. He's in business, you must meet him, you'll like him.'

My turn had come at the counter, and I paid.

'You must forgive me, but I'm in a hurry, I have to get back.'

'Do you still live in the same place?' Elizabeth asked.

I explained that we had just moved, and that we didn't have a telephone yet.

'Give me your number,' I said, to avoid annoying her, 'and I'll call you.'

'Promise?'

'Promise.'

She scribbled it down and gave it to me. I stuffed it in my pocket, smiled at the little girl and left.

I contrived somehow to lose the telephone number, by accident or design. Why would I want to see her again? What still amazes me is her reaction. Was it simply social convention? She spoke as if the entire past was forgotten, as if everything that had once united us, then driven us apart, had never existed.

It's true that I remind myself of my mother. My mother always used to say: 'I don't bear malice, but I have a good memory.' Perhaps she was right? What good is forgiveness, if it simply means forgetting everything?

Friday 16 July

These recent years would have been perfectly peaceful if I had not continued to suffer from sleepless nights. Robert is now a successful journalist, much in demand. He has been promoted several times and has a brilliant career. In fact it is his success which has made it possible to buy the house we have just moved into. For some time we were looking for a bigger apartment in Paris. But when the possibility arose of moving to the countryside, we couldn't resist it. The decision was made quickly and unexpectedly. One of Robert's colleagues was selling his parents' house; he mentioned it, we went to look at it, and a week later we were exchanging contracts. It has meant my leaving my job, of course, to look for something nearby, but I am quite happy with the prospect of a change. As for Colette, she starts at the lycée in Versailles in September.

Colette is fifteen now, a grown-up young lady. She is very like Robert: his eyes, his smile. She took up painting again two years ago and would like to go to art school when she has done her *baccalauréat*. This choice makes me very happy. Because it reduces my guilt? Perhaps that is part of it. If what I did had destroyed her vocation for good – and for some years I thought it had – I would never have forgiven myself.

To celebrate her return to her love of painting, I have had the famous canvas repaired. It is a pretty picture, very sensitively done. The light seems to shine out of it, the branches of the cedar protect a peaceful world, and the two little girls, now restored, give this motionless scene the touch of life it would otherwise have lacked.

Saturday 17 July

We left the rue de Vaugirard without having time to sort everything out, each of us had an allotted area, Colette saw to her bedroom, Robert to ours, and I was in charge of the sitting room and kitchen. We packed everything up, papers and books accumulated over almost ten years, objects and souvenirs, the packing-cases piled up for three days and the removal men have dumped everything in the main room here. We practically packed the dust off the shelves.

At first I had a system: I numbered the cases and listed their contents. But as time pressed, I gave up, and so did Colette and Robert, so we have ended up here in such confusion that the first week I thought we would never see the end of it. Luckily Colette was here to help. Taking advantage of the space we have and the fine weather, which means we can use the terrace, we began by making piles: outgrown or unwanted clothes to be given away; papers to throw out; books to sell or give away; toys to be given away or thrown out, depending on their condition.

At the bottom of one case I came across Louise, Colette's old doll. Overcome with dizziness, I had to sit down on the floor, in the middle of everything.

'What's the matter?' asked Colette, coming in.

'Nothing, I'm just tired.'

Tired was an understatement. I felt suddenly weak, so weak that I couldn't control my voice, I was on the brink of tears. How can an object from the past, a battered doll, with its eyes and one arm missing, and its dress torn, 'a stupid old doll', as we used to say at home in Belgium, upset me so much? Colette came up, saw Louise on my knees, and took her away. Did she understand? I try to be rational with myself: my emotion is not caused by this discovery, but by the stirring up of the past that comes when one moves house, the old photograph albums one finds, the letters one re-reads, the broken objects one cannot bring oneself to get rid of, the memories. Is Colette as sentimental as I am? I hope she does not throw Louise away.

Sunday 18 July

This morning I got up later than usual. Since I only managed to
fall asleep at dawn, I needed some extra rest, and I took advantage
of the Sunday calm to stay in bed, re-reading old papers. By the
time I came down, Robert and Colette were at the end of the
garden, still in their pyjamas, busy with a big bonfire.

'Mummy, come and see!'

I could tell by Colette's voice that her eyes were shining and I
could understand her delight in having a garden where one could
burn old things, and go out without being properly dressed. I
went down the garden in my dressing-gown, the air was cool, but
the day promised to be hot.

'Come and see.'

Robert was fanning the flames, while watching out for stray
sparks. The smoke that arose from the fire was of different
colours, thicker or thinner depending on what was burning.

Suddenly, in the middle of the pile, I saw the doll Louise, half-
melted with the heat. Without thinking, I went closer, leaned
over and reached out to rescue her.

'Look out!'

Robert was shouting, he grabbed me round the waist and
started hitting me, I struggled, what was he doing?

'Get your dressing-gown off, quickly!'

In a few seconds my dressing-gown had caught fire. I had just time to slip my arms out of the sleeves before becoming a living torch.

'Your nightie! Get the nightie off!'

Before I could move, Robert had torn it in two and was pulling it off me. Our cries had aroused the neighbours and there I was, stark naked on our lawn, under the startled gaze of a man looking over the hedge.

'Do you need any help?'

Colette burst into hysterical giggles, while Robert stood in front of me to hide my nakedness from prying eyes, and gave me his dressing-gown, which I quickly put on.

'Are you all right?'

Yes, I was all right. I had felt the heat of the flames, but only a few hairs had been singed. Robert turned to the neighbour. 'Don't worry, we are all right. It was the bonfire ...'

'I see,' said the neighbour in a slightly knowing tone.

Colette went off into another fit of giggles and ran into the house. Robert and I looked at each other, and began to laugh as well, the neighbour, looking disapproving, had disappeared behind the hedge, still, if we want to avoid having a terrible reputation here from the start, we must make amends, invite them round for tea.

'What on earth got into you?' asked Robert as we went into the house.

'I don't know, I think it was the sight of the doll burning in front of my very eyes, I couldn't stand it.'

Robert put his arm around my shoulders. I welcome his affection, but the impression I sometimes have that he treats me as a war victim irritates me sometimes. The victim was not me, nor even my family or my people: every human being, if humanity is allowed down this path, is a potential victim. It does not simply happen to other people. If only we could learn that from the cradle, if each of us had this truth imprinted in his or her flesh, then we might be able to live together. In peace.

Monday 19 July

What can 'Jewish consciousness' mean to someone like me, who was not brought up in the religion or even the culture of the Jewish people? Solidarity with persecuted innocence, yes, something like that. A feeling rooted in me since childhood.

Tuesday 20 July

Last night before supper we went round to knock at the neighbour's door. A woman opened it. I offered her three roses from our garden and introduced myself:

'I'm Hannah Périer and this is my husband, Robert Périer. We are your new neighbours.'

A look of understanding came over her face.

'It was you, yesterday ... ?'

'Yes, it was.'

'Ah, yes, my husband told me.'

I laughed. 'He must have found it a funny sight! I am so sorry ... '

'Oh, don't worry about it. You weren't hurt, I hope? Do come in,' she said, opening the door wider. 'My husband is not back yet but he won't be long.'

We drank an apéritif with them and invited them to come round later on when we had finished moving in. They seem to be simple, ordinary people, without any complicated history.

Thursday 22 July

Last night, to celebrate the Belgian national day, I made a *waterzoi*. I had trouble finding the recipe, and in the end it was one of Robert's colleagues, Chantal, who does the cookery column on one of the weeklies, who found it for me. It must have been a success, because we talked about nothing else during the meal but recipes for tasty dishes and memorable meals from the past. After supper we lingered on the terrace in the cool of the evening. After recipes, we began to talk about Belgium, and Colette asked us questions about the war for the first time. Robert sat drowsily smoking his pipe and digesting, and I was the one who answered her.

Until then I had never spoken to Colette about her origins. I did not think it worth while, since she had not asked. Now that she was asking me, it was time to tell her. I explained how and why I had changed my name, how her father had been in the Resistance, how in the end I had joined it too, and that all our lives had been at risk. When I explained that, according to Jewish law, she is Jewish too, because she has a Jewish mother, she did not seem shocked. Robert on the other hand came out of his doze and reacted in a way that surprised me.

'Why are you putting that sort of idea in her head? Colette

isn't Jewish, don't be ridiculous!'

There followed a painful exchange which leaves me with a bitter taste in my mouth. Why was he so anxious to deny something that has marked our lives so cruelly? His reaction upset me so much that I ended up defending an extreme position.

'If we could persuade every Frenchman that he has Jewish blood in his veins – and I'm sure there is a lot more than people think – these things would never happen again.'

Robert just laughed.

'Sweetheart, don't be silly.'

'I'm not the one who's being silly,' I retorted. 'If you persist in telling your daughter that she isn't Jewish, what is to stop her becoming anti-semitic in the future?'

That stopped him, and he swallowed before replying.

'Well, her honesty and her goodheartedness. I didn't have to be Jewish to join the Resistance, did I?'

He's right, of course. But I am not wrong. When people are in the mass, I am less confident of their goodheartedness and judgement, and more inclined to ask about their uncontrolled reflexes. Was not a large section of France in the pay of the Nazis for five years? And by being an accomplice for four years of a criminal power, France can surely be said to have lost the war?

'How can you say such things?'

This time, Robert is really angry:

'If that was the case, why did you celebrate the Liberation? And the victory in '45? Didn't we fight on the right side, as we should have done? Didn't we get the Nazis out in the end? Didn't we put them on trial?'

I did not reply at once. I have no intention of quarrelling with Robert, especially since he fought Nazism with a courage that I have always admired. But I want him to understand me. He turned to Colette.

'What complicates it, you see, is that your mother's family was deported, and she has never got over this terrible event. So, of course, she can't be objective.'

I feel like screaming. But I know that would only strengthen the argument – in my view scandalously simple-minded – that

Robert is putting forward. And I know he is sincere. So I try to take a deep breath and speak calmly.

'You're mistaken when you think that you are being more objective than I am. You are just taking the short-term view.'

And I set out my point of view. France has been defeated three times by Germany: in 1870, as nobody would dispute; then again in 1914, when defeat was transformed into victory only at the last moment, thanks to American intervention (after all, in 1918 the Germans were 60 km from Paris, a lone monument in the plains of Champagne still stands to tell the story, and if the Germans did not continue their advance and take the capital, it was because their army was paralysed by divisions inside the general staff); and lastly in the 1939 war, when defeat was as sudden as it was devastating, and the occupation lasted five years. What would have happened to France if the Americans had thought they would do better to let the Europeans massacre each other? The countries that really won the war were Britain and the USA; they alone avoided collaboration with the Nazis. Every other country was affected, contaminated, France most of all, something that should never be forgotten, and we should avoid false legends which prepare the way for real crimes.

We went on arguing late into the night. Robert was responding to me but his anger had fallen away, he knows that I am right, he knows, because he has lived through it, that men are only too eager to deceive themselves and to stifle the truth under their desire for power. Colette listened, asking questions from time to time. How many French families remain haunted, like me, by the fear of a revival of this murderous hate? Anti-semitism is endemic in France, always liable to break out again. There was the Dreyfus Affair, there was the anti-semitism of the 1930s, and there was the Occupation. The victory freed the country from its demons for a while. But when the memory has faded, when those who witnessed it have grown too old to remember, or have died, will they not arise again? If they ever do, I hope Colette will remember. France lost the last war. Because the true war was waged on French soil, and no victory, no treaty, no signature at the bottom of a document can ever wash away a past that can only be prevented from repeating itself if we keep the memory of it alive.

Wednesday 28 August

How can one resist the temptation to forget, while at the same time avoiding being obsessed by one's memories? I am desperately trying to find the right balance between the two, but I have not yet succeeded.

But this balance is what one must aim for.

Because forgetting prepares the ground for repetition, while obsession makes for a poor kind of memory, one so painful that it produces the desire to forget.

Friday 30 August

I must be the best-informed woman in France about the remedies for insomnia. I think in the last ten years I have tried every kind of sleeping pill they make. But it is no good, I still sleep just as badly. Or else I have to take so many pills that I am doped not only at night but for the rest of the next day.

I have also tried all the folk remedies. Walking out in the dew in the early morning, drinking a spoonful of olive oil before going to bed, eating apples or raw onions, not to mention infusions or counting sheep (I have surely counted more sheep in ten years than there are on the globe!), nothing seems to work for more than a day or two. I have concluded that only a dramatic change in habit may sometimes, inexplicably, make a difference.

I have not lost all hope yet, though. Medicine has made such progress in recent years. Surely someone will come up with a more effective cure soon.

Monday 6 September

In two weeks, Colette will be back at school.
I am looking for a job.

Wednesday 8 September

Yesterday afternoon M. and Mme Durieux, our neighbours, came to have tea with us. They admired the garden, Madame gave me some advice about plants for the flowerbeds, Monsieur talked to Robert about pruning the trees. Even Colette behaved perfectly: she set up her easel on the terrace and unconsciously contributed to this stereotyped image we are constructing.

When it grew cool, we went indoors and Robert lit a fire in the grate. Madame sat close by it, rubbing her hands to warm up, while Monsieur looked round the room, politely examining the pictures and objects. He stopped suddenly in front of the Christmas picture.

'Ah, that's interesting. Have you been to La Charmoie?'

La Charmoie? Since we looked puzzled, he explained.

'Yes, it's a beautiful house, not far from here. Where did you find the picture? It's very pretty and a good likeness.'

Luckily Colette was still on the terrace and had not heard. I did not dare tell him that our daughter had painted it – he would not have believed us or would have thought we were crazy. Robert evidently had the same thought, since he replied:

'I found it in a junk shop, but I don't know where the house is. Can you visit it?'

While Monsieur Durieux was explaining how to get there, I went into the kitchen, on the pretext of boiling some more water. My ears were ringing and my head began to ache suddenly. What has got into Robert? I certainly never want to set foot in the place.

Friday 10 September

I have just met M. Durieux and my legs are still trembling. I was just closing the garage door when he passed by.

'Did you go and see the Jew house?'

I felt my blood freeze. Unable to speak, I just gaped at him.

'You know, La Charmoie, the house in your picture. Oh, didn't you know? Before the war the people there were Jews. Say what you like, the war was a good thing in some ways. At least we got back some of our heritage. I think a count bought it afterwards, some sort of aristocrat anyway. Well, that had to be an improvement!'

And I thought he was a man 'without any complicated history'. I didn't realize how literally true that was. I will tell Robert tonight. Never again will we speak to these people.

Sunday 12 September

I realize that since I have taken up this journal again, I have not set down a word about Louise, and yet Louise lies behind everything in these pages, without her I would probably have written hardly anything at all. Am I afraid to confess to myself that she is still part of my life? By not sharing this secret with anyone else, has it become such a burden to me that I cannot even bear to admit it to myself?

It is true that there are days when Louise is a burden. This burden is like an extra life, wasted because it is impossible to do anything with it. Louise is a burden to me as a treasure would be if it were locked up in a chest, in a land where people were dying of hunger. She is a burden comparable to useless and scandalous wealth.

And yet, as misers in the old days used to lock themselves in with their hoard of gold coins, just to look at them and plunge their hands into the pile, with a delicious pleasure that cannot be told, I find myself, as I drop off to sleep, cultivating that half-way state between dream and reality and calling Louise to my rescue before I start the day.

Every year she has gone on living for me at night, growing up; she was eleven years old in June, and on Midsummer Day she blew out her candles. Everyone was there, the living and the dead, around the white table-cloth – my parents, Isabelle, Robert and Colette, even Michel, my real family, all present.

Last year Michel got married. His young wife is called Nathalie, she teaches philosophy. They came to dinner in the rue de Vaugirard not long before we moved and we said we would keep in touch. All these years Michel has gone on being discreetly but quite actively supportive, a confidant, but also someone who gives me good advice, with my interests at heart. He is a truly loyal person. One of the very few in the world.

For the last weekend before school starts – Colette goes to lycée this Monday – Robert decided that we would go for a drive. We visited the Palace at Versailles – the gardens were beautiful with autumn leaves, it was fantastic. On the way back, when Robert hesitated about the route to take and started to get lost on side-roads, I had an inkling of what he was doing.

'No, I don't want to go there, surely you know that. Absolutely not.'

Colette asked from the back what I was talking about.

'Nothing, I'll tell you later.'

Robert looked over his shoulder.

'It's a pretty place our neighbour told us about, but your mother for some reason ...'

When Robert is in this kind of mood, 'teasing' me, he calls it, sadistic, I call it, I really hate him.

'I warn you, if we don't go straight back home, I'm going to jump out of the car.'

He looked at me, saw my hand on the doorhandle, and realized from my expression that I meant it. Giving in, he shrugged his shoulders.

'You're being quite ridiculous.'

This evening I found in his pocket the directions M. Durieux had given him, and confiscated them. This way, unless Robert asks Durieux for them again – which he surely cannot, after what I have told him about his opinions – I am unlikely to be treated to any further nasty surprises.

Friday 15 October

I have found a job now, in a pharmacy in Versailles. I begin next month. Two more weeks of freedom.

Monday 18 October

It is midday, I am on my own, sitting on the terrace enjoying the last sunshine before winter, and the silence. Robert went to Nice last night, and will be away two days. Colette will not be back until seven.

This morning, sorting out my clothes, I found in the pocket of my blue skirt the directions for going to La Charmoie. Why didn't I throw them away? The paper was crumpled, but when I flattened it out, the map was still readable. 'The Jew house.' The war did not kill the demons after all. It even worked in some people's interests. 'At least we got back some of our heritage,' he said. I recall with horror the conspiratorial wink he gave me, which left me open-mouthed. Why couldn't I react. Was it still the same old fear? Is it stamped on my flesh by history?

And yet, it's true, I really am unable to understand something. Something to do with the human capacity for evil, which I still cannot take in. How can this man, who seems so good-natured, who appears perfectly sincere, how can he use such disgusting language? There must be some insanity somewhere, something like an infectious disease, that takes over weak-minded and credulous people. I can't believe that he dreamed up his ideas himself. I can't believe that if he had been brought up differently, he would not have defended the opposite point of view. I can't believe that he has enough intellectual resources to realize the enormity of what he said. He must have been led astray, he is weak, easily influenced. A man of limited intelligence, who has heard sick people spreading this ideology which gives him the illusion of being strong, and as a result he has become one of the bastards himself.

I can't say that I decided to go. I had the map on my knees, then I got up, thinking I would make some coffee. On the way to the kitchen I passed the picture, and paused. Was it really possible that this place could exist? Before thinking, I had picked up the car keys and locked the house. I admit, too, that when confronting this mystery, a mystery which I feel belongs to me alone, I felt stronger. Above all, capable of stopping and turning back if the emotion became unbearable.

It was not hard to find. About fifteen kilometres from our house, a small side-road led away from the main road and through a wood. A few hundred yards along, there was a board: 'La Charmoie, Private Property'. From the road, unfortunately, I could see only some tall wrought-iron gates, behind which an unmade track turned sharp right and went into the trees. The house would be beyond.

'Did you want to visit?'

I jumped. Behind me was a boy on a bike, I had not heard him coming.

'If you like, I can let you in.'

'You live here?'

'My parents are the caretakers. The owners are never here during the week. They live in Paris. Rich people.'

I accepted and followed the boy through the gates. After walking about fifty yards through the trees, I saw at the edge of the wood the cedar tree, then the house and terrace. I went on a little, looking round to the left.

'Isn't there a little pond down that way?'

Surprised, the boy slowed down and looked at me.

'But I thought ... Have you been here before?'

The resemblance between the house and the picture is hallucinating. Inexplicable. But the oddest thing of all is that this discovery only slightly surprises me.

I followed my guide a few steps further, looking for the fishpond, and still not finding it. In the end I did see it, rather further away than in my dreams, if I dare say so, and bigger. There are no water-lilies. My guide looks at me inquiringly.

'If you want to ask about it, you can come in. My mother will be there ... '

He nodded towards a little lodge which I had overlooked, perhaps because it was never there in my dream. Yet it did not seem to have been built recently.

'If you are sure it would be no bother?'

A woman of about forty was already at the door, and, seeing me with her son, looked suspicious.

'Did you want something?'

Her son explained. I asked her to forgive my curiosity:

'Our neighbours told us about this house. And we have a picture of it at home, so I thought I would like to see the original ... '

Her expression became more welcoming and she invited me in.

'I was born here, my parents were caretakers before me.'

'And you were here during the war?'

She looked at me oddly, visibly wondering whether I could be trusted. I noticed a photograph of De Gaulle on her sideboard and decided to chance it.

'Well, I ought to tell you, I am Jewish and ... '

This admission operated like a password. But she decided not to speak in front of her son.

'Georges, could you go and fetch the bread, please.' When he had left: 'Do you know about what happened?'

I told her what the neighbours had said and my conversation the next day, but without using the insulting words. The very mention of what had happened brought tears to her eyes. She brought out a handkerchief.

'I'm so sorry, I can't help it. It was the little girls, you know, there were two little girls, so sweet, I used to babysit for them. I was paid, of course, but I loved them. They were nice people.'

She sniffed.

'Nobody ever found out who had given them away or why. I thought everyone loved them. They were funny, kind, the lady was always smiling, they had plenty of money but they were generous with it and didn't look down on people. I still don't understand.'

'Really? You never knew?'

She looked at me for a moment.

'The worst of it is that now I don't want to know. I know everyone in the village and have done since I was little. So what if I were to find out that it was somebody I know, someone close to me?' One day I even dreamed that I had given them away myself. Can you understand?'

I have no answer to this fear, which she confesses to me as if it were reprehensible. One day this war will have to come to an end. I got up to go, thanked her and she walked me to the door.

'The new owners are not bad people. They bought it after the war.'

'Who from?'

'I don't know. After they were taken away, the house stood empty for a year, then people started coming to see it. We just stayed here. When these owners bought it, they kept us on. In spite of the past, we wanted to stay because it was our home, after all. My son was born here.'

She accompanied me to the gates.

'So you live near here?'

I explained that we had recently moved to a village not far away.

'Well, you are welcome to come back. My husband would be glad to meet you.'

I made a non-committal reply, and thanked her for inviting me in. But why would I want to come back? On the way home I thought about the closed shutters and wondered if the house was like my dream inside as well, probably not. And anyway, what did it matter? This place has no other truth than the history I have just heard, which is strangely parallel to my own. But the strangest thing of all is not this meeting, not even the coincidence that has brought me to a real house just like the one I have dreamed about, since after all there must be hundreds of houses

188

in France that look much like this one. The oddest thing of all for me is that the history I share with this other family who vanished during the war, along with so many others that I do not know about, this whole history of the deportation and murder of a couple and their two little girls, can be considered by us, by human beings, as a commonplace story.

Tuesday 19 October

Last night, after finishing her homework, Colette came to see me in my bedroom. For some years now she has been in the habit of doing this when Robert is not there, taking advantage of a quiet evening to come and talk to me. As time has gone by, we have gradually got to know each other differently, each of us discovering what the other is like, beyond the conventional family relationship, more like a friend or an equal.

It was during one such evening in 1952, in early May if I remember it right, that she raised the subject of Elizabeth.

'I never really liked her, you know. I was afraid of her.'

'Afraid?'

'She had forbidden me to talk to you. She said that I had already hurt you enough with the picture.'

'And you believed her?'

'I don't know. No. But I was frightened.'

Yet I remember their apparent complicity, at least at first. And Colette's pleasure, every time Elizabeth visited us. How closely does what she says now correspond to the truth? Perhaps it doesn't matter. What matters is today's truth, even if it is a reconstruction. All history is a reconstruction. What she was telling me then, what I was hearing, was that she had made her

190

choice. And that she loved me.

If until then there had remained some distance between us, maintained by our silence, from that day on she has trusted me totally once more. But she does not confide in me for everything. Colette remains a reserved, secretive person. But we do exchange ideas and opinions. I try to pass on to her my values, in which I still believe.

Last night, for instance, she wanted to know why I had never had another child after her. Why did she ask me this? What did she know? What did she imagine? Had she already asked Robert? I don't know. She never speaks about things that touch her directly and deeply. She always comes at things in a roundabout way, never made clear to me, but which I accept, as one accepts that other people have a different way of being in the world.

I simply gave her the immediate reason, which was true: that I couldn't have any more children. Surprised, she asked why. I had to think for a moment before replying and telling her the rest of the story. I told her how I had been pregnant in 1943, how at the time it was very difficult for us to think of having a child, and then told her about the decision we had taken, and the abortion, which had probably had some damaging effect on my future fertility.

'But did you want to have the baby?'

She asked me this, as if despite all the precautions with which I had surrounded the story, some hint of regret or remorse had crept into my account. I gave a careful answer, as truthful as I could make it.

'Your father was right, we were in too precarious a situation. And if I had really wanted the baby, I would have gone ahead with it. Your father didn't drag me to the doctor by the scruff of my neck, you know ... '

By giving her this version of events, which today I am unreservedly prepared to accept, I realized that I, too, have changed and reconstructed my history. Otherwise, loving Robert as I always have done, how could I have survived?

Tuesday 23 November

In the long saga of my attempts to find a medical solution to my insomnia, there was an episode last week which is worth noting down. On the advice of the pharmacist with whom I work, I consulted a reputed neurologist, who has published some important studies on sleeplessness. After my first visit, he explained that nowadays there is a very effective kind of treatment, which usually means a single injection, in the scalp, to obtain immediate and lasting relief. After my sigh of satisfaction, he added that in some cases a second injection might be necessary, three days later. And in any case, if I needed a second injection, that would definitely deal with the problem.

I was, of course, very impressed and agreed to have the injection. For the first couple of nights, there was no improvement. The first night I went to sleep only at about two o'clock, the second at about three, after having gone to bed obediently – and in complete confidence – at eleven. As arranged, the third day, I called him and he told me he would expect me at the surgery for the second injection, which would really do the trick.

Once more, the first night and the second went by without any change. Since on the third day I was passing his surgery on my way home, I decided to call in without an appointment and see whether he would see me again. The receptionist opened the door, consulted him, and let me into the waiting room.

'The doctor can see you very quickly, between two other appointments.'

I waited about an hour, then he called me in.

'So,' he asked triumphantly, 'things have improved now?'

I smiled sadly: 'Alas, no,' I began, 'that's why ... '

'What do you mean, no?' he exclaimed. 'It's impossible!'

Before I could say anything, he had fetched a book from his shelves.

'Look! You can see it's impossible! I've written a whole study on this treatment ... I've published the results of all my patients over five years!'

I couldn't help laughing.

'I can't argue with that, but I'm afraid I am still having sleepless nights.'

He looked at me disdainfully, and with a deeply offended air, then cleared his throat and, with flashing eyes, spat out:

'You are wasting my time. I don't believe you.'

I was expecting anything but that. Was he mad? I can see no other explanation. Dumbstruck with surprise and repressed fury, I got up and left without another word.

When I recounted this to Robert and Colette at dinner, they laughed till they cried. I laughed with them, of course, but as one laughs at a satire, with a bitter feeling that behind this farcical behaviour, exactly like one of Molière's doctors, there lies the tragic reality of uncontrolled medical power, which can be exerted with impunity in the secrecy of the consulting room.

1962

Saturday 3 March

Louise is ill. Every night for a month now I have been dreaming that I am sitting up with her, she has a fever all the time, she shivers, she hardly ever laughs, her cheeks are burning, her eyes are too bright, and I don't know what is wrong. Every morning I wake up with anguish in my heart, as the day goes on, it fades somewhat, but it is becoming more persistent, and it comes back in full force, with burning intensity, at night.

Doctors, familiar or not, have come to Louise's bedside – all the ones I have consulted over the last twenty years and some I haven't, even Michel, and all is in vain. There is no sign of this high fever being relieved by any medicine, it gives her a headache, but she does not complain, simply smiling weakly when I lean over her, but saying nothing. Why am I so frightened?

It's true that I used to be scared – when I began to dream about Louise, then when I realized that she was not disappearing, that she was growing up, that she would never leave me, I feared for my sanity, for my family and for my life. I used to wish then that I could stop dreaming about her, that I could plunge into sleep like a bottomless pool, the kind of sleep that pills provide, and that was why I kept asking for regular prescriptions, but I wished for this, I now realize, as one wishes for the impossible, without really wanting it to happen. I did not really want her to disappear. Perhaps I simply wanted her to take her leave of me, or that she should never to have existed. But not that she should die. And now that I sense her life is threatened, now that the fever seems to be consuming her more every night, as her eyes are becoming hollow, it is the same fear that has returned to grip me: the fear that I will not survive her death.

The state of tension this keeps me in has not gone unnoticed by Robert, but he is not over-concerned by it. He puts it down to Colette's approaching marriage, and perhaps he is partly right. She is marrying a young architect, David Kaufmann, and moving to Paris. It is true that her leaving home will be a blow, the more so as I am trying not to let it show, and I am happy about it, too, happy for her, since she seems to have made a good choice, and happy for us, Robert and me, since we shall now have a chance to rediscover each other in a different way. But only on condition that I can rediscover myself? I suppose that is why I have started writing this journal again. Whenever I have felt lost, I have hoped that writing would rescue me or at least support me somehow, but perhaps that is just one more illusion.

Writing is not a crutch. Writing, too, only exists on condition that it is an extra life.

Like Louise.

Wednesday 7 March

Louise is still ill. This morning, for the first time in years, I woke up with tears running down my cheeks. Robert leaned over, anxiously wiping them away.

'What is it?'

I opened my mouth, for a second I thought I was going to tell him everything, Louise, the last twenty years, but no words came out, everything would be too much, every day the burden increases. I kissed him, and pulled myself together, nothing, a bad dream, I've already forgotten it. A few words, saying what he expected, were enough to reassure him.

Luckily the wedding preparations are keeping me busy. It is in a week's time. Colette and I have organised everything: we will have a wedding lunch here and in the evening a reception at David's parents' house. They live in a big house in some grounds somewhere near here. I haven't met them yet, but I have spoken to Mme Kaufmann several times on the phone. She sounds nice, young.

Thursday 8 March

As I do every year at about this time – is it because springtime gives me new hope, or is it lassitude after another year ruined by insomnia? – I have made an appointment with a doctor. Since that crazy specialist who gave me injections in the scalp, I have seen a whole series of consultants: neurologists, psychiatrists, homoeopaths, acupuncturists, but nothing seems to work. So this time, I'm doing something more straightforward. David – my future son-in-law – has recommended his GP, a 'good family doctor', he says, who has treated him since he was a boy. I telephoned and was given an appointment in three weeks. In any case, after so many failures, it can do no harm.

Thursday 15 March

One thing is certain: life has no meaning. If it did have even one kind of meaning, we would not spend our whole existence inventing new ones, every day that God makes. This is really the strange thing: the faculty we have for fitting ourselves into events, thinking of them as a sequence, when they are simply a succession of effects without a cause; we imagine that meetings or coincidences have a secret logic that rules the world, when such a logic is no more than a projection of our own desires, a child's dream merely, as old as time, haunting our minds. So why on earth should I be looking for some kind of meaning in the fact that, by some combination of circumstances that completely escapes me, David's parents bought La Charmoie two years ago?

In fact, for a few days now I had been suspecting something like this, some kind of secret preparation. Since Robert telephoned Monsieur Kaufmann to ask how to get to their house for the reception on the evening of the wedding, I had felt something was being kept from me. Was it because of Robert's smiles? Or the questions he kept asking Colette about the place where the reception was to be held? It's impossible to say, especially since, after the event, one's judgement becomes clouded and provides precise reasons, claiming that they are objective, whereas at the time there could be a thousand possibilities. Even my impression that 'I suspected something' is no doubt coloured by the surprise I had when, on the evening of the wedding, after the lunch at our house, Robert drove us up to the gates of La Charmoie.

'What ... what are you doing?'

Smiling, Robert opened the car door for me.

'It's here.'

At once I thanked heaven I had been here before: at least this would enable me to keep my emotions under control. Shutting my eyes for a moment, I pictured again the house with closed shutters, the cedar, the pond and the caretaker's lodge. Would the woman I had seen before still be living here? Would she recognize me? I remembered then that Robert knew nothing about my visit years ago, and decided not to tell him yet. After all, he was playing some kind of joke on me, secretly, by this surprise. Well, I would pay him back and surprise him by my calm reaction.

It was getting dark and the guests were beginning to arrive, we went into the grounds.

The young couple were already waiting for us at the door, radiant with happiness. I kissed Colette and greeted David, who took us over to his parents. Robert did not take his eyes off me.

Later on, when the young people began to dance, I asked Mme Kaufmann how long they had been at La Charmoie.

'Two years,' she replied. 'When we set eyes on it, we fell in love with it: a lightning romance!'

'Lightning is the word for it,' said M. Kaufmann, joining us, 'literally.' And he told me how the first winter they were there the cedar had come down in a storm.

'It was a magnificent tree, hundreds of years old. I'll show you the stump when you come and see us again. We couldn't get it out.'

I did not dare tell him that I already knew about the tree, and carried on asking questions as discreetly as possible.

'I noticed a little house in the grounds ... '

Mme Kaufmann's face fell.

'The caretakers' lodge?'

They were there no longer. A mysterious tragedy had befallen the family just about the time when the Kaufmanns had bought the property.

'It was in the papers, don't you remember?'

No, I had seen nothing about it. She explained: the son had killed his father with a shotgun, then turned it on himself. The mother had had a breakdown.

'The papers suggested it was something to do with denunciations during the war, but they didn't give any details. Then the matter was hushed up, you know the way these things are.'

Yes, I know.

Later again, Colette came to see me, flushed and out of breath from dancing, and very happy.

'You'll have to come back again. The house is lovely, when you see it in daylight. It reminds me a bit of my picture, I mean *your* picture,' she corrected herself, laughing. 'Well, vaguely. Tell me if you agree.'

'Vaguely', she said. Her impression is surely more accurate than mine.

Tuesday 20 March

This evening Colette and David came to see us. They looked excited and had news for us. Before Colette said a word, I had guessed. She is pregnant, three months now, but she didn't want to say anything until she was sure. And not before the wedding anyway. I was surprised, but rather pleased, that she had the tact to respect people's conventional sensibilities, which I didn't think I had passed on to her. We got out some champagne and drank their health, I was overcome with emotion, full of happiness that made me want to cry.

Thursday 22 March

I am worried. Colette called last night. She has had some pain and lost a little blood. She sounded very depressed. I told her to lie down and keep still, and to call Michel to come and see her. I hope he will be able to examine her today.

Friday 23 March

Michel telephoned to reassure me. According to him, as long as Colette rests and stays lying down, things should be all right. But she shouldn't be painting: standing up for any length of time is not advisable for the moment.

I called Colette, and she sounded better. I will go over on Saturday.

Monday 26 March

I have just come from the hospital, Colette has had a miscarriage, Life is too unfair.

David had called me from the hospital at the end of the morning. Feeling better, and sorting out some pictures for an exhibition, Colette had made an awkward movement, and that seemed to have started it off again. I left a message for Robert and rushed to the hospital. She was still in theatre, and they were carrying out a curettage, I think. I waited with David in the corridor. He was stricken, worried about Colette above all. At last the doctor came out.

'Monsieur Kaufmann?'

David went over and I stayed where I was, not wanting to interfere. They spoke for a few minutes, then David nodded and came back.

'Everything is OK, she's still a bit groggy from the anaesthetic, but they're taking her back to her room.'

He sat down beside me on the bench and lit a cigarette. I was not looking at him now but thinking about Colette. We must help her to get over this shock, she is young, she will surely be able to have children. And here, after all, she has been properly looked after. I was marshalling my arguments, imagining our conversation, when I heard David mutter:

'Apparently it was a boy.'

I looked at him, he looked at me, and, before thinking, I heard myself saying:

'David, please believe me, don't tell her that. I beg you.'

Distracted as he was, did he listen to what I said? He looked at me in a puzzled way, got up and began pacing up and down.

Wednesday 28 March

Colette is back home. As David was at work, I took the day off myself to take her home, using this excuse to see her. She is not feeling too bad, and taking it philosophically. I almost had the impression that I was more upset than she was. When I left, she hugged me and said:

'Don't worry, my dear mother, you'll soon be a grandmother. A bit later than we thought, but quite soon'.

May God grant it.

Thursday 29 March

This afternoon something has happened to me which, without realizing it, I have been waiting for for twenty years; and yet at the same time I had given up waiting for it. I am so overcome that I hardly know where to start.

I had an appointment at two o'clock with David's doctor, a Dr Boyer. I had never seen him before. I found a middle-aged man, kindly, with a friendly manner, the sort of man you pass in the street every day, who looked much like many other doctors I have consulted. He welcomed me in with a firm handshake, asked me to sit down and, as all doctors do, asked what seemed to be the trouble.

So far, this was nothing new. Every year I have found myself in the same situation, facing an unfamiliar doctor to whom I describe my medical history and my many and varied attempts to overcome my sleeplessness, which seems resistant to any cure. I now have my story word-perfect, going into more or less detail depending on the questions asked. Dr Boyer listened carefully at first without interrupting, then when I had finished, he asked a few questions about the different treatments I had tried. Apparently satisfied with my replies, he then said nothing for a while. How long, I couldn't say exactly, but long enough for the silence to start to seem unusual. I had no more to say myself, I was waiting for his verdict and for him to prescribe the latest wonder drug from our laboratories, but he went on saying nothing. Still saying nothing, he looked at me as if he was thinking, then suddenly his eyes sharpened and he asked me in a voice that sounded strangely gentle:

'Tell me, why are you unable to sleep?'

Why? Nobody had ever asked me exactly this question. They had asked me how I slept, what time I went to bed and got up, when I fell asleep or wakened, did it change with the season, but why I couldn't sleep, no, no one had asked me that.

Dr Boyer did not take his eyes off me. As if he already knew. Not the precise reason, perhaps, but that I knew something I wasn't telling him.

Something that might help him, and help me.

At any rate that is how I am explaining the scene to myself afterwards, but at the time I was simply taken by surprise, astonished, and the astonishment increased as I heard myself starting to tell the story which until now I had never told anyone: the story of my dreams since the abortion, the secret life of Louise. It was not easy to tell, it was not the kind of story you spill out with pride or even the pleasurable relief of the confessional, no. I had to tear it out of myself as if I were vomiting, and I kept bursting into tears, as if my whole body was conspiring to expel this impossible dream.

Dr Boyer did not interrupt a single time. He simply listened to me with remarkable intensity.

When I reached Louise's illness, which has now been haunting my nights for weeks, I stopped.

'That is where I am now. That's all.'

And as if the tears and the words came from the same source, my tears stopped at the same time as the words.

Dr Boyer remained silent for a moment or two, giving me time to wipe my eyes and collect myself, then he asked me:

'You had never spoken about any of this to anyone before?'

I shook my head, no, to nobody. Ever.

'Good,' he said, getting up. 'I would like you to call me next week and tell me how you are sleeping by then.'

'You are not going to give me anything to take?'

'No. Don't take anything. Don't take anything for the time being,' he repeated, 'and give me a call.'

When I left the surgery, still shaking and unsteady on my feet, I looked at my watch and saw that he had kept me there for almost two hours.

Friday 30 March

I slept well last night. I dozed off at eleven o'clock and woke at seven.

Saturday 31 March

Another good night. Off to sleep at midnight, woke up at half-past seven.

Thursday 5 April

I telephoned Dr Boyer. For the first time in twenty years, I have
been sleeping properly for a week.

Tuesday 30 October

Six months of sleeping normally, without dreaming, have transformed my life. Or at least my outlook. And for the first time, in all these years, I felt like reading through this entire diary and starting it again. I have gone back over awkward or scribbled sentences, correcting some things here and there, looking for the simplest and most accurate. way to express what I have been thinking or feeling. In this revision, I have encountered a feeling of peace and relief that nothing else has ever brought me.

In 1948 I was asking myself whether it was possible to bridge the gulf between myself and my family created by the inner drama of my dreams about Louise. Looking back on it, this diary itself, a daily record which has taken on its own form, seems to me to be my attempt to do precisely that. For it to succeed in this aim – an aim I have unconsciously been pursuing over the years – Robert will have to read it. He will have to understand it for what it is.

It is too soon yet for that.

Sunday 1 November

I gave in yesterday to the others and agreed to go and see the Resnais film about the camps, *Night and Fog*. It was Colette in the end who persuaded me. She was determined to go and see it at the Cinemathèque, and Robert said he would drive us there, so I allowed myself to be convinced. After so many years the scars must surely have healed, the wounds closed. Almost twenty years have passed now since my parents and sister vanished, and although I have never seen their bodies or discovered exactly where they died, I thought I had grown used to the idea. As time passed, I thought of them a little less often, and even if Isabelle's smile, glimpsed on an unknown face, could sometimes move me to tears, or if my father's voice or mother's laugh, overheard in a crowd or on a bus, sometimes made me jump and set my heart racing, I honestly really believed that I had accepted the reality.

But there are some wounds that time cannot heal, some wounds that reason cannot reach. When at the end of the film the bulldozer was sweeping away piles of corpses, it was not the sight of this collective horror that made it hard for me to breathe, but the realization that I was twisting my head to try to identify the bodies and to recognize my family among them.

Monday 12 November

This story must come to an end here.

I don't think I can ever start this diary again. These notebooks were really the writing down of Louise, of an inner adventure which other words, spoken now, have released for good, have loosed into the atmosphere. These notebooks were also the price paid for the crime, the crime I shared with Robert, but for which I am probably the only one responsible.

For seven months now I have been sleeping normally and have had no more dreams about Louise.

Epilogue

Hannah Périer, née Gomperz, my wife, died ten years ago in January 1981, after fighting cancer which kept recurring for fifteen years. She was then sixty-four years old.

Shortly before she died, she gave me this diary. Reading it, I discovered someone I did not know, very different from the person with whom I had shared my life for over forty years. To say that I felt regret would not be accurate. Hannah had made me very happy, and although our marriage went through some bad patches, I always took them to be necessary episodes, signs that the bond between us was still alive. Never, in my mind, did they threaten our partnership. I was twenty-five when we first met, and when I chose her for my wife, I knew it was for good.

So although I had no regrets of that kind, my first reaction when I read these pages was none the less to feel aghast at her inability to confide in me, or rather at the doubt which had overcome her and prevented her from sharing with me this obsession which was eating away at her. What an appalling waste of time! I said to myself when I reached the last line. If only she had told me about what was happening to her at the start, would she have been spared all this suffering?

This question must have been readable on my face when I went back to see her in hospital, the next day, for she simply whispered – she was very weak indeed by then – 'At the time you wouldn't have understood.'

219

As I pretended to agree with her, in order not to upset her, she still had enough strength to whisper with a smile, 'Have you any strudel for me?' Then she closed her eyes and opened her hand for me to take it. Everything had been said.

She lived for another three weeks. Three weeks of a struggle which I dare not call pointless: perhaps in order to accept death, one needs to rid oneself of all hope, even the glimmer of it. It was a struggle in which I shared almost every moment, perhaps because I was the only person there who was able to, perhaps because I felt in this slow approach of death almost an initiation ritual enabling me to live with the inevitable permanent separation that was coming, perhaps because I have always been, as Hannah herself wrote, 'a very conscientious person'.

And it is also because I am conscientious that I have finally decided to publish this text. I do so to pay homage to her courage and discretion, and to her talent. I have not, needless to say, cut or changed a line, even though I do not always come out of it very well. I do not think I need to justify anything. The man referred to in the pages of the diary is not the same one who is writing these lines, even if we bear the same name. My truth is not her truth, but if I accept this disillusion today, I have only recently understood its depth and its inevitability. In the past, it would have seemed to me to be a lack of love.

So Hannah was right. At the time, I would not have understood. By keeping silent, she was protecting our love, or rather my love for her, which was sincere and deep, but also fragile and clumsy. By letting her words speak today, I want to do justice to a love which was always shared, but justice above all to the rare quality of that love.